Alexander Macdougall Cooke DM FRCP

MY FIRST 75 YEARS OF MEDICINE

Alec Cooke

Fellow of the Royal College of Physicians

ROYAL COLLEGE OF PHYSICIANS

Royal College of Physicians of London
11 St Andrews Place, London NW1 4LE
Registered Charity No. 210508

Copyright © 1994 Royal College of Physicians of London
ISBN 1 86016 006 9

Typeset by Oxprint Limited
Printed by the Lavenham Press

Contents

Alec Cooke

DM FRCP

Physician, icon and colleague

An editorial note

Why is the College publishing this autobiographical account of an exceptional innings in medicine?

In 1995 Dr Cooke will celebrate his Diamond Jubilee as a Fellow of the College. So it is no great surprise that for some years he has been the most senior Fellow present at the occasion of the election of the President of the College on the Monday after Palm Sunday. It is the senior Fellow's task to give thanks to the retiring President for his or her year in office, a task which he continues to fulfil with grace and eloquence. Anyone who has had the privilege of hearing Dr Cooke on these occasions will have admired the fluency of his delivery – naturally without a note in his hand – and will have been aware that this was no anodyne homily of pretty, but empty phrases. His eyesight may not be as sharp as it once was, his hearing not as acute, but little escapes his observation or fails to be recalled from his memory, honed by seventy-five years of medical practice and almost seventy years as a Member and Fellow of the College, during which he has served the College as examiner, councillor and senior Censor.

It is our good fortune that Dr Cooke has given us the opportunity to publish the recollections of his seventy-five years in medicine, presenting us with an eye-witness account of the breakneck changes that have taken place in medicine, science and social conditions since the early days of this century.

Alexander Macdougall Cooke was born in 1899 on October 17th, the day before St Luke's day. It was therefore almost predestined that he would become a great physician. Now, after his 95th birthday, he has begun a new diary which we hope to publish in October 1999.

ROBERT MAHLER FRCP
*Editor of the Journal of
the Royal College of Physicians*

Alec Cooke – My Icon

By David Pyke CBE FRCP

Physician and former Registrar of the
Royal College of Physicians

I became Alec Cooke's senior registrar on St Luke's Day 1952, his 53rd birthday (Alec's I mean, not St Luke's). It was one of the luckiest days of my life. It was the beginning of an enchanted period (for me). I have been learning from Alec ever since, not only about the history of medicine (he lived so much of it, as this book shows) but also about the present and the future. I recall him talking about the medical application of electron spin resonance 40 years ago. Here was a man talking about the very latest thing in medical research who had known medicine before the treatment of pernicious anaemia or even diabetes. Yet he claimed to be opposed to 'progress'; when patients at St Thomas's Hospital were being fed raw liver in the 1920s for their pernicious anaemia, he said: 'Whatever will they think of next?'

He says that the luckiest day of his life was when he was appointed to the Radcliffe Infirmary in Oxford, but he must have forgotten his wedding day. Vera was the perfect foil for Alec—she was the only person who ever got the better of him, which she did always and effortlessly. He was at Oxford as an undergraduate, trained at St Thomas's, failed to get on the staff there which, I am sorry to say, he now regards as a stroke of great good fortune, then came back to Oxford at the age of 33 and is still there. At that time there were three full physicians at the Radcliffe— Hobson, Mallam and Cooke—and one assistant physician, Teddy Buzzard. I hear that now there are more than three. Through all the changes of transforming the Radcliffe Infirmary of those days into the John Radcliffe Hospital of today, and the upheaval in medicine which dictated it, from the tiny medical school of a few dozen students (mostly from overseas or young dons who did not want to leave Oxford and had no intention of becoming physicians) to the enormous and enviably respected student community of today, Alec has been sitting quietly at the centre of things, an inexhaustible source of dry, wise wit.

He is a clinician above everything—superb at the bedside, listening, talking and teaching. As all great clinicians do, he prides himself on his history-taking, but he was once defeated, when examining in the

Membership, by a loquacious but inarticulate patient. Determined to understand his problem, Alec finally asked him: 'What do you chiefly complain of?' The patient thought for a while and then replied: 'My wife'. Alec's teaching was famous. Every Tuesday and Friday afternoon he showed cases to the pre-clinical undergraduates as illustrations of clinical physiology. They loved it. Those who were up at Oxford 30 or 40 years ago still remember those demonstrations. They brought meaning to their pre-clinical work and fired their enthusiasm for clinical medicine. Alec could always do that because of his own enthusiasm. I suppose he must have been bored sometimes, but I have never seen it.

Most people in his position are swept on to a wider field than their own clinical responsibilities. They become heads of large departments, members of important committees, advisers to the government, officers of international societies. They take to the air and return to base only to refuel. Not so with Alec; he stayed here — although I remember once when I wanted to see him I had to go to London to do so, but at least it was London, not Tokyo or Sydney or New York. Perhaps part of the reason for his way of life is that he does not like committee work. He says he is no good at it. He either falls asleep or argues furiously about something that was decided at the last meeting which he had not attended. The happy result is that Alec did not become an office-holder, an Important Man. True, he held office in the Royal College of Physicians where he became Senior Censor (First Vice-President). When he was asked to give the Lumleian Lecture of the College in 1955 he was worrying about the encroachment of the specialties on general medicine. His topic was osteoporosis. He wanted to call it 'The bare bones of medicine' because, he said, that was all that was left to the general physician — and that was 40 years ago.

Alec ran the diabetic clinic at the Radcliffe, not because of his own enthusiasm so much as because someone had to do it. Of course he became enthusiastic and enthused those who worked for him, myself included. What added to the enchantment of working for him and with him were his *obiter dicta*, his comments on life and above all his Laws. He enunciated the first two Cooke's Laws himself: 'It costs more than you think' and 'It takes longer than you think'. There are no exceptions to either Law. They provide guidance in life for us all, Chancellors of the Exchequer, hospital managers and housewives. His Laws have spawned other laws. My own Cooke's Laws are: (1) that all public actions have only one effect, the opposite of that intended (If you doubt this, recall Barbara Castle and private practice in the NHS, or Henry Cohen and subscriptions to the GMC); and (2) that all treatment tends to be continued. Alec is a master of English, spoken and written, and is strict with anyone who offends against the language. That makes him the ideal trainer for the young doctor who has to write or present a paper. Directly or indirectly he is, I believe, greatly responsible for the extremely high standard of papers given to the Association of Physicians. He is equally helpful with his career advice: 'Get to 40 as quickly as you can and stay there,' or 'if you are cornered in an argument, imitate the action of the squid and emit a cloud of words.' Two more, seemingly trivial, comments are actually among his most important: after he had had a wisdom tooth extracted he declared: 'A minor operation is an operation done on somebody else.' And even more telling, to anyone who stopped him in a public place complaining of pain in the chest, opening one shirt button and asking 'Is it all right?' (corridor medicine, he called it) he used to reply: 'If you will come to my room and take off all your clothes I will try to find out', adding 'Medicine with the clothes off is difficult enough, with the clothes on it is impossible.'

Despite being a non-office-holder Alec Cooke has had an enormous influence on men and medicine. Ask anyone who was at Oxford or at the Royal College of Physicians at the relevant time about him. Their faces will light up and they will start telling you some new Cooke story. It is entirely right that when David Weatherall and his colleagues were producing their great new book, *The Oxford Textbook of Medicine* in 1983, they asked Alec to write the introduction. It was a tribute to their judgement to choose him and to his to write as he did. His sense and sensibility shine through these quotations from that introduction: 'Physicians do not treat diseases, they treat human beings'. 'In a perfect world no one would qualify as as doctor or nurse without having been ill, experienced bewilderment and fear, or faced the rigours of modern investigation and treatment.' 'There is a strong case for keeping alive purely clinical medicine, that is diagnosis by the history and the five senses (of which common sense is the most important).' 'Whatever technological empires are built the most important person in the hospital will still be the patient.'

Perhaps Alec's zest for life is best encapsulated in his remark at a lunch party held to honour his 90th birthday: 'Life has been extremely interesting. I should have been furious if I hadn't been born.'

I envy the readers of this book. They can look forward to the pleasure of getting to know Alec Cooke and his first 75 years in medicine. Lucky them!

DAVID PYKE

Alec Cooke – My Colleague

By A. H. T. Robb Smith FRCP FRCPath

Former Nuffield Reader in Pathology,
University of Oxford

It has been my good fortune to enjoy Alec Cooke's friendship for nearly sixty years, for in 1937 it was he who first welcomed me and revealed to me the Oxford atmosphere when I came to the Radcliffe Infirmary as a 'Nuffield importee'.

In 1933 Dr Cooke was appointed the first May Reader in Medicine and Assistant Physician to the Radcliffe Infirmary. The general practitioners in Oxford soon realised that they had in him a superb consultant physician who always saw their patients' problems and their illnesses as a whole. Patients, too, felt complete confidence as he gave them his undivided attention, made careful notes of everything and gave them a realistic and objective assessment. Although a general physician, his particular interests were in metabolic disorders. He started the first diabetic clinic in Oxfordshire at the Radcliffe Infirmary in 1941 and also made important studies on osteoporosis and the circumstances relating to fractures in elderly persons.

In 1929 Sir William Morris had purchased the Radcliffe Observatory and its grounds, giving parts to the Radcliffe Infirmary and to the Board of the Faculty of Medicine. In 1935, now Lord Nuffield, he gave £8000 for a new medical ward (Collier) which Dr Cooke designed with the greatest care for his patients—and a very fine ward it is. Sadly, by the time it was ready for occupation the Nuffield Scheme had come into being and it was allotted to Professor Witts while Alec had to be content with either a hut or some of the old wards.

As a teacher Dr Cooke was outstanding. His formal lectures were superb and his ward rounds always full of unexpected information. But probably his greatest contribution to medical education was when, as May Reader, he introduced clinical demonstrations in anatomy and physiology for Oxford medical students reading in the Honours School of Animal Physiology or the first BM. The students would come to the Radcliffe Infirmary and he would have selected a patient, not so old or so ill as to be disturbed by being examined by students, perhaps to display the consequence of a major nerve injury, or a goitre (Thames

Valley Disease) or mild congestive heart failure. For the students these were memorable experiences.

Early in September 1939 it was decided that the London teaching hospitals should be evacuated; on September 21st at an informal meeting in Dr Cooke's house at 123 Woodstock Road, it was agreed that Oxford medical graduates could have their clinical training at the Radcliffe Infirmary; and on October 2nd Dr Cooke, newly created Clinical Subdean, was ready to welcome the first group of clinical students to the 'Isle of Man'. This consisted of four rooms in Somerville (Ladies) College providing a lecture room, a museum, a common room and an office. He cherished the embryo clinical school in its difficult early years, championing it strongly when it was nearly destroyed by the Board of the Faculty of Medicine, saw it safely into Osler House (formerly the Radcliffe Observer's residence) in 1948, and was able, by a letter to *The Times*, to prevent the gardens being covered with huts for a nurses' home. His approach to teaching and clinical medicine was common sense applied to an unusually high degree, achieved by a unity of understanding which enabled students to see what medicine was about; the minutiae might be omitted but seldom were, and there was always a clear perspective and insight.

In his active days at the Radcliffe Infirmary whenever you might meet him, there was always something entertaining or exciting to discuss, however short it might be, for he never wasted time and frequently looked at the envelope which was his aide memoire. An indefatigable traveller, his friends would receive postcards reflecting his enthusiasm for architecture and with a witty succinct phrase in the style of the famous Cooke's Laws that have given many of us direction and pleasure.

Dr Cooke was editor of the *Quarterly Journal of Medicine* for many years. He has strong views on the proper use of English in medical writings and had no hesitation in a powerful application of the editorial blue pencil. His own writings, impeccable in style, clearly reflect his broad interests. He has also very strong views on the need for decorum in hospital surroundings, so he is bitterly against whistling, shouting or running down corridors and the like.

In his younger days Alec took part in all kinds of sport, but when he returned to Oxford he limited himself to squash and judo. It was in the 60s that two Fellows of the College questioned his ability in the gentle art and found themselves painlessly but firmly on the floor of their senior common room. There was always a warm welcome in which his wife Vera and the family joined at his home at 123 Woodstock Road, and this atmosphere of hospitality has continued in his subsequent homes to the present day. Essentially a clubbable man, Alec is very content in his Fellowship at Merton College, and he belongs to a number of dining clubs which can offer variety from the Merton fare.

During the last decade, Alec has been much occupied with his autobiography and clinical memoirs. But as a senior member of the University he continued to take his academic responsibilities seriously, joining in the Vice Chancellor's procession at Encaenia and only this May returned his vote for the Professorship of Poetry. He celebrated his 90th birthday with a visit to India. Last year, in a Norwegian steamer, he inspected the Lapplanders with their herds of reindeer at Nord Cap. In September this year (1994) he has just returned from a Mediterranean cruise.

When Alec returned from London to Oxford sixty years ago the Radcliffe Infirmary was a country hospital of less than 300 beds without a clinical school. Now it is the United Oxford Hospitals with a notable undergraduate clinical school which he created and an internationally recognised postgraduate research school. Through all the years of change Alec's gentle enlivening presence has provided a cornerstone of Oxford memories for friends, colleagues and generations of students of medicine.

A. H. T. ROBB SMITH

MY FIRST 75 YEARS
OF MEDICINE

Dedication

*To the memory of my daughter Jean, whose last
task before her untimely death was to go
meticulously through my manuscript and
correct numerous small errors*

Thanks

I have received generous help from my son-in-law Theodore Rowland-Entwistle, from Mr William Lund, FRCS, Mr Malcolm Gough, FRCS, Mr John Burgass, librarian of Merton College and Mr Geoffrey Davenport, librarian of the Royal College of Physicians of London, and his assistant, Miss Teresa Sutton.

A.M.C.

NOTE
Throughout the text asterisks appear against names.
These indicate that brief bibliographic details
can be found in Appendix 1.

Prologue

What, another medical autobiography? Why? Authors can be presumed to have some reason for writing – to augment their reputations, to make money, in the case of doctors to increase the number of their publications, to transmit knowledge which they think the world lacks or would be better for knowing, even for revenge or for the *cacoethes scribendi* – in modern parlance 'just for the hell of it'.

My own motives are twofold. First, to fill a gap. My father was born in 1852 and my mother in 1858. It never occurred to me during their lifetimes to ask them what the world was like in their younger days, in the latter half of the 19th century, now more than 100 years ago. I deeply regret this foolish omission. To the young modern reader, the 84 years since I made up my mind to do medicine will seem almost an equally long way off.

My second reason is that, like most medical men and women, I have found medicine the most fascinating subject in the world and an enthralling occupation, so much so that I cannot resist thinking about it, talking about it and, as a corollary, writing about it. That is my apologia.

I made up my mind to do medicine at the age of eleven, and I have no idea why. There were then two medical men in my family – my uncle, Cecil Cooke, who was our family doctor, and the husband of a Scottish cousin – but neither of them influenced me in any way.

I started badly as an idle, ill-behaved, unwashed and thoroughly disorganized schoolboy. I must have been a worry to my poor parents. I went to the Merchant Taylors' School, then in Charterhouse Square in the City of London. I started on the Classical Side which I did not much enjoy, but I am now grateful for the Latin and Greek which enabled me to get into Oxford. Two of my school reports tell some of the truth. The first – 'He might have done better, but I doubt it'; the second – 'I take him to be quite an intelligent boy who does just enough work to keep out of trouble.' I still think that this showed considerable judgment.

At the age of sixteen I transferred to the Special Side, that is, the Science Side. Throughout my school career I was influenced less by the

...idle, ill-behaved, unwashed and thoroughly disorganized

interest of the subject than by the personality of the teacher. I took to science like a duck to water and was fortunate in my teachers. To everybody's surprise, not least my own, I gained a scholarship to Jesus College, Oxford, and one to St Thomas's Hospital.

I left school in 1917. It was during World War I, so of course I had to join the army. My first and freezing night in the service of His Majesty King George V was spent sleeping on a bare stone floor with no bedding of any kind. If you turn to the semi-prone position so that you are not resting on your hip bone, it is not at all bad. What it is to be young! I started my military career as a private in the Royal Fusiliers at Hounslow Barracks but after careful thought decided that square bashing was not really my metier.

I then transferred to the Royal Flying Corps and was stationed first at St Leonards-on-Sea, East Sussex, in a large Victorian house. It was a com-

2

paratively comfortable billet, but there I had my first experience of homesickness. While trying to shave in a small housemaid's pantry, with no window, no light, no mirror and ice cold water, I was seized with an overwhelming desire to go home. I managed to resist but had an unhappy 48 hours. Ever since I have felt for my children when they were going off to boarding school.

Great stress was placed on physical fitness, so we did physical jerks each morning on the roadway outside our billet. I was noted less for my gymnastic ability than for usually having to do my press-ups where a horse had recently passed. Other activities included playing football wearing gas masks, and doing cross-country runs from one map reference to another. I was not much of a runner but I could read a map. On one occasion 1,000 men started but 997 got lost. I came in third, a long way behind the first and second runners. On the strength of this athletic feat I never ran again but organized the running of my unit. Our military activities were basic drill, military law and the like. I was a keen young man and was promoted to underofficer, but caught measles and was sent to what was called a fever hospital. This was actually a disused drill hall with no mod. cons. We were not ill and had no recreations and so we were very bored. Our only entertainment was being hypnotized by a fellow-patient. I was an easy subject because I could relax and make my mind a blank, or perhaps it was that anyway. On my return from the fever hospital I found that I had lost my rank, but this is just life.

We then moved to Oxford where I was stationed in the Queen's College in some comfort. It was the only barracks where we were summoned to meals by a silver trumpet. Here we learnt about the Morse code, rigging, aero engines, bomb aiming and other aeronautical matters.

In the spring of 1918 Oxford was struck by the influenza epidemic. One Tuesday morning hundreds of the cadets in the various colleges were simultaneously struck down. Those who remained well till lunch time were not affected. In some of the epidemics of that period there were many deaths, and the 1917–18 world influenza epidemic caused more deaths than the war. In the Oxford part of the epidemic there were only a few deaths. I was afflicted, and remained in bed, unwashed, unfed and unattended, for five days. On getting up to have a wash I saw in the mirror a haggard looking young man with a stubbly red beard.

We next moved to Uxbridge, Middlesex, where we fired machine guns through rotating propellers, and by a magical device never hit them. Then came the great day when we were issued with flying clothes, beautiful fleece-lined garments, necessary because all planes then had open cockpits and were extremely draughty and cold.

The airfield was at Brockenhurst in the New Forest. We started on Avro trainers, almost foolproof machines that could land at 45 miles an hour and had a skid in front (like an outsize ski); if you landed too steeply the skid hit the ground and turned up the nose of the aircraft. There were many pupils and the weather was not always suitable for beginners to fly, so we spent some of our time with a camera gun. This looked like a machine gun but took photographs of aircraft, and showed you how well you were aiming. We then moved on to dual-control Sopwith Camels. I was getting on nicely and looking forward to my first solo flight when the war ended, and all training stopped, so I never fired a shot in anger – just as well.

The war finished on November 11th. Anxious to get home, I paid daily visits to the orderly room and became such a nuisance that the adjutant eventually said 'Take a railway warrant and for heaven's sake GO AWAY.' I reached home on November 27th, 1918.

A medical student at Oxford

I came up to Oxford in January 1919. Jesus College and Oxford University formed agreeable changes from the military life. They did not start so early in the morning, but at Jesus College there was a choice – either roll call at 8.0 (early but short) or chapel at 8.15 (later but longer). After a short time ex-service men were spared these indignities. My first term was rather empty because few of the undergraduates had managed to get out of the services so soon. Next term was much better. Many of my contemporaries were young men of 23 who had commanded battalions in action because all the other officers had been killed.

I came up on the chemistry ticket but, as had always been my intention, changed to medicine. I had distinguished teachers. Five were Fellows of the Royal Society, and one of them, Sir Charles Sherrington*, was the current president. The Regius Professor of Medicine was Sir William Osler*. My first encounter with him was on a fine spring day in 1919. I was walking up Parks Road to the laboratories when I saw coming towards me an elderly man in full academic dress accompanied by a lady. When they were about 30 feet away the man suddenly threw his arms apart and skipped along like a child, chanting 'The Sun, the Sun, the glorious Sun', quite oblivious of everybody else. His wife walked on unperturbed.

Osler used to hold a ward round for students and general practitioners at the Radcliffe Infirmary at 10 o'clock on Sunday mornings. I attended some of these. In one we were taught how to examine the abdomen: if right-handed the examiner should stand on the patient's right side; and the most important things to remember were clean finger nails and warm hands. This may sound elementary, but it was good medicine. Osler died in December 1919 and was succeeded by Sir Archibald Garrod* from St Bartholomew's Hospital, who in 1909 had written *Inborn Errors of Metabolism*, a book which opened an entirely new chapter in medicine. Garrod was a sad man because he had lost two of his three sons in the war, and the third had also died. His daughter, Dorothy, was a distinguished archaeologist who became the first woman professor of archaeology at Cambridge. Garrod did not have much contact with the students, but on one occasion we were summoned to a lecture room to hear an address about medicine. It was interesting, but some of us were a little shocked when at the end of his discourse he expressed the hope that we would all make a lot of money. This hope has not been realised in my case.

While at school I had done the preliminary subjects – chemistry, physics, botany and zoology – at London University. Because I was an ex-service man I was allowed to count them as equivalent to the Oxford preliminary examinations and did not have to take them again. So my two subjects for study were physiology and anatomy. Not surprisingly, I found the former the more interesting.

The Oxford teaching had six parts. First, lectures; fortunately they were not compulsory. Sherrington, although a distinguished scientist and a delightful man who always talked to students as though they were his equals, was not a good lecturer. In the lecture room was a plastic lay figure whose organs could be removed. Sherrington would stand with his back to the audience, contemplating the lay figure, then remove the spleen, study it carefully and continue lecturing on the reciprocal innervation of antagonistic muscles. We all attended his lectures solely out of admiration and regard for him.

The Professor of Anatomy was Arthur Thomson*. At the beginning of each term, whether he was down to lecture on the vascular system, the respiratory system or the digestive system, he always started with the ovum, and he had a unique collection of early embryos. Alas, by the time we had safely got the polar bodies out, the end of term had come and we progressed no further. The lecture list also announced some lectures at Wadham College, but we were warned on no account to attend them because the lecturer was very old and would have been much upset if anybody had attended.

Second, we did simple experiments on frogs' legs to demonstrate some of the basic physiological facts. Third, Sherrington had devised a more elaborate course on mammalian physiology. We used decerebrate cats on which to repeat some of the classical experiments, and also acquired some manual dexterity. In both these practical classes the results were recorded on smoked drums, the pen being a straw with a little piece of stiff paper at the end, cut to have a point. There was no nonsense about electronics. Fourth, we did what was called 'histology'. This consisted of cutting, mounting and staining animal tissues embedded in wax. It took so much time that little was left to examine the results under the microscope. Histology is really microscopic anatomy and is now taught in that department.

Fifth was the tutorial. Jesus College then had no medical tutor, so I was farmed out to Dr C.G. Douglas* of St John's College. I went to him at 9 o'clock on Monday mornings. While I read him my essay he ate a large breakfast and read *The Times*. We then had a discussion. The sixth consisted of reading textbooks and, more importantly, original papers. We began to learn how to find our way about the world's medical literature. I use the word 'literature' because it is common usage, but most medical writing by no stretch of the imagination deserves this title. We also learnt the important fact that all the contents of books and papers are not necessarily the received truth.

In anatomy we dissected the whole body in what we regarded as unnecessary detail. Is it really essential for a doctor to know all about the cutaneous nerves of the thigh or the origins, insertions, nerve supply and blood supply of the small muscles in the sole of the foot? In my time dissection was thought to be an indelicate subject. Queen Victoria had written of:

> 'the awful idea of allowing young girls and young men to enter the dissecting room together, where the young girls would have to study things which could not be named before them.'

In accordance with this view, the women students had a separate dissecting room and a female teacher, Dr Alice Chance (later Carleton), but in 1937 the dissecting room became common to both sexes. Alice then taught the men as well. She was a witty Dubliner, much admired but sometimes feared. She had had a curious educational career. Her father was president of the Royal College of Surgeons of Ireland, who for some reason, I think on the occasion of a conference, had received an honorary degree at Oxford. He was impressed by the place so, looking round his large family, he nominated Alice to go to Oxford to read English Literature. She came up to Somerville College and at the end of her first academic year went home to Dublin and put on the hall table a pile of books that she had brought for vacation reading. Her father picked up the top book which was a Jacobean play called *'Tis Pity She's a Whore* and said: 'This will not do. English Literature is off. I shall give you a *viva* on the humerus after dinner.' Alice qualified in medicine in 1916. She was a good teacher. It was the practice that when a student had completed the dissection of some part of the human frame, he faced a special and much-dreaded *viva* from Alice. On one occasion a *viva* on the female pelvis concluded with Alice saying: 'Mr Smith, your ignorance does you great credit.'

Oxford has always had an interesting tradition of 'learned tradesmen'. When I was an undergraduate I bought my toothpaste from Druce's, a chemist's shop in the High Street. Mr Druce was an amateur botanist of such distinction that he was a Fellow of the Royal Society.

About this time I scored my first medical success. My natural modesty does not prevent me from recording it. There was a railway strike. I was an ardent strike-breaker and became a porter at Euston Square station. A fellow porter was a pleasant young man. When he found that I was a medical student he insisted on confiding his troubles to me. He was engaged to a girl; they were deeply in love, her parents approved of him, his parents approved of her, and every prospect was rosy except in one respect – every time she ate strawberries she felt very ill. Could I give any advice? I suggested the solution of not eating strawberries. They had never thought of that and he was embarrassingly grateful.

In 1920 I took physiology finals and, by what the BBC calls 'a slight technical hitch', was placed in the first class. I then concentrated on anatomy. I also had the privilege of becoming one of Sherrington's demonstrators because the regular demonstrator had taken to drinking the absolute alcohol in the laboratory and in consequence required inpatient psychiatric help. I was only one step ahead of my pupils, some of whom later achieved great distinction.

In 1920 I took physiology finals ... and was placed in the first class

Also at this time I became the medical tutor of St Hugh's College, then a college for women only. Before World War I, if there was a male tutor a chaperone sat in the room with them. By 1920 morals had become so lax that the chaperone sat in the next room in case there were cries for help.

At this time, just after the war, there was a shortage of bodies for dissection because the number of medical students returning from military service amounted to an entry of four years at one time. Anatomical teaching was therefore organized in Paris and off I went with two Oxford friends. In London each medical school has its own dissecting room, but in Paris teaching is in a single institution, *L'Amphithéâtre d'Anatomie des Hôpitaux.* Any body fished out of the river Seine, whether drowned by accident or suicide, seemed to arrive at the Amphithéâtre. There was such a generous supply of cadavers that one department when giving a course of instruction in ear, nose and throat surgery used only the head and neck; the rest of the body was discarded.

We were taught by an elegant young surgeon. He was beautifully dressed and we greatly admired his boots of black glacé leather with cloth tops and pearl buttons. His method of instruction was simple. He said: 'Messieurs, voici le so-and-so. C'est très intéressant, très important. Très important au point de vue d'anatomie, de chirurgerie et de pathologie. Très intéressant. Très important.' In this way we went round the whole body.

We also studied surface anatomy at the *Folies Bergères,* revues mostly devoted to the female form divine. These nude and shapely young ladies were very beautiful but visually not half as sexy as one might suppose. They were in the same league as the Venus de Milo or Velasquez' Rokeby Venus. On the other hand the verbal humour was extremely improper. I could not sully these pages with examples.

Undergraduates are very fond of founding societies. I remember two to which I belonged. The first was the Neo-Hellenic Society where we read each other excruciatingly intellectual essays on literature, art and life. The other was the Phidippedean Society. Phidippedes, you will remember, was the first man to run a marathon, and he DROPPED DOWN DEAD. The club met on Sunday mornings and drank a bottle of sherry while planning the next week's runs. The only rule was 'NEVER run today'.

One of the most important things I learnt at Oxford was about alcohol. When I attended the dinner of a literary society I had never been exposed to alcohol before and became for the first (and last) time in my life very, very drunk. My last recollection was of walking unsteadily across the restaurant. To regain my balance I took hold of a table, but missed it and managed only to grab the tablecloth. Everything on the table crashed to the floor. I then became unconscious. My kind friends took me back to college and put me to bed, but could not bring themselves to deal with the vomit. I awoke next morning thinking that death would be a merciful release. The ensuing three days of nausea and malaise produced a complete and lasting cure. When I was at my worst, a clergyman friend called. It must have been obvious to him what the situation was but, being a humane man, he would insist that I had an unusually bad attack of influenza. Afterwards it was alleged by my friends that although I could hardly stand up I would keep talking, chiefly saying: 'My mind's quite clear, but I can't control a word my body does.'

In the Long Vacation I stayed up to do a course in pathology, bacteriology and pharmacology, really an excuse to enjoy the summer in Oxford.

A medical student at St Thomas's Hospital

In the autumn of 1921 I repaired to St Thomas's Hospital in London for my clinical work, my choice determined partly by a family connection with that hospital and partly by a scholarship. In Oxford we had studied the scientific background of medicine. Here we were to see real, live patients.

I already knew some of my fellow students from schooldays or Oxford days. A large proportion were public schoolboys or had been to Oxford or Cambridge. They tended to have good manners and knew how to talk to people. A surprisingly large part of medical practice consists of talking to and dealing with people. As I used to say to each of my new house physicians: 'Your work will largely consist of dealing with people – the patients of course, but also their relatives, the ward sisters, the nursing staff, your fellow house officers, ME, the registrars, the consulting staff, the laboratory staffs, the hospital administrators, the porters, the Press and even the coroner.' Today, medical students come from a wider social background. They become technically competent but do not always have good manners and tend to be less good at communicating with people.

The St Thomas's Medical School was a friendly place, with a club and a restaurant. The waitresses were Cockneys with a sharp sense of repartee. From overhearing endless medical 'shop' they had acquired a remarkable amount of medical knowledge. One of my fellow students was a very short and very fat little man. I once said to a waitress 'Have you seen Mr X this morning?' Her reply was: 'Mr X, is that the gentleman with the ovarian cyst?'

Like all students we got up to mischief. In the entrance hall of the hospital was an old carriage that had been used by Florence Nightingale* in the Crimea. The students introduced beside it an old motor car, filled its gearbox with plaster of Paris and labelled it 'Used by Sir Percy Sargent* at the Battle of Waterloo'. The matron was not at all pleased, and when she saw a nurse laugh at the car she ordered all nurses not to walk past it, but to go up the staircase before it and descend the staircase after it. Medical students have the reputation of being rather wild young men (I don't know about the women students), but on the day they qualify they instantly become professional and proper.

Of course I had to belong to a night club, the Cave of Harmony in Charlotte Street, run by the actress Elsa Lanchester and Charles Laughton, the actor (later her husband). The club provided music and dancing, and plays were performed. There was not much alcohol. The proceedings began when most sensible people were going to bed and ended about 5 o'clock in the morning. As I then had to walk home to Hampstead it was not long before my enthusiasm for the night life waned.

Teaching was by the good old-fashioned method of apprenticeship. Lectures were compulsory but not popular. I once heard an exasperated St Thomas's teacher say to a student: 'The trouble with you Oxford men is that all you have been taught is not to believe what you have been taught' – a splendid tribute to that university. Sometimes the attendance book contained 35 names but there were only five persons in the lecture room. As in most educational establishments, none of the lecturers had ever been taught how to lecture. At Newcastle-upon-Tyne the Professor of Civil Engineering used to give an annual lecture on *How not to lecture*. He arrived late, tripped over the dais, dropped his notes, all the slides were irrelevant or upside down and he went on too long. This was amusing but had most beneficial effects. I wrote and asked him to let me have a copy of his script so that I could adapt it for medicine, but he would not part with it.

For instruction in the infectious diseases we had to travel to a neighbouring fever hospital. The journey was always enlivened by passing a large and handsome building which announced its function in gold letters as TRAINING COLLEGE FOR MISTRESSES. We used to wonder what went on behind those high walls. There were four one-hour lectures on the subject of vaccination for smallpox. The essentials could have been taught in a quarter of an hour, but it was obviously difficult to spin this subject out for so long, so the lecturer started by showing pictures of the sheds where the cows were kept.

Our first introduction to patients was as clinical clerks. I started on the firm of Dr Charles Box*, the senior physician. The first patient allotted to me was a girl with advanced leprosy. Her fingers had withered away and were only about half an inch long, but still had deformed little nails. Box's career makes one realise how recent the history of medicine is. He qualified in 1891, five years before X-rays were discovered. In the 1920s he thought that this newfangled device was not a bad dodge if you had mislaid your stethoscope but probably not necessary if you had taken a proper history. He had been house surgeon to Sir William MacCormac*, a St Thomas's surgeon who had practised surgery in pre-Listerian days, wearing an old bloodstained frock coat with the ligatures threaded through the buttonhole and (Box assured me) with his dog sitting under the table. Lister's* paper on antiseptic surgery was published in 1867, so two and a half professional lifetimes take one back to the dark ages of surgery.

Incidentally, the advent of X-rays was world news. The notion that one could actually see through things caught the public imagination. In the United States one state immediately passed a law prohibiting the use of X-ray opera glasses in the theatre, and an enterprising English entrepreneur made good money by selling *X-ray-proof underclothing especially made for the sensitive woman.*

I so much enjoyed my clerkship with Box that I did a second three-month term. For surgery I was a dresser to Sir Cuthbert Wallace*. He used to ask his students what were the two surgical discoveries that had given most relief to the human race. We suggested the obvious – antiseptic surgery and anaesthesia. The correct answer was false teeth and spectacles.

I entered for the Mead* Medal, generally regarded as the top prize in medicine, and much to my surprise won it. I also gained the Toller* Prize. I was presented with the medal by the president of the hospital, the Duke of Connaught* the only one of Queen Victoria's children with whom I have shaken hands. Carried away by this success, I entered for the corresponding surgical prize, the Cheselden* Medal. The first part of the exam was to do a dissection. We drew lots and I was given the structures on the inner side of the ankle, a particularly easy task. I made a most elegant dissection. When the Professor of Anatomy came to inspect the exhibits he was accompanied by a friend of mine who was one of his assistants. My friend reported that when the professor looked at my work he said: 'That is the man who knows no anatomy; they always make these absurdly neat dissections.' The next part of the exam was a *viva* on surgical instruments, about which I knew nothing. I was shown a Lane's* cleft palate needle holder, a queerly-shaped pair of tongs terminating in two small cup-shaped jaws. I had no idea of its function. Determined not to show my ignorance I said with great confidence: 'Ah, yes. That is a special instrument for removing very small gallstones from the gallbladder.' The examiners gave way to what I thought was most unseemly laughter. I did not win the medal.

One important aspect of student life was the Christmas show, a revue in which the senior medical staff were pilloried and mocked. They rarely objected; what really hurt was being ignored. There was one occasion when the ophthalmologist did take exception to the alleged discovery in a dark room of his department of a patient who had waited so long that he was a skeleton. Great trouble was taken with the programme. There were bogus advertisements, for example notices of operations – Mr Z for retroverted bowler, and that the favourite reading matter of two members of the staff known to be at violent loggerheads was *Chums* (a popular children's comic of the day).

In about August some twenty students appeared to give up their studies to concentrate on the Christmas show. My contributions were various – as scene shifter, prompter, performer, part author, stage manager and producer. In the last capacity I was determined to have a stage horse. Unfortunately the two young men inside not only quarrelled but got drunk, with the result that they fell over the footlights on to the élite sitting in the front row.

During my student days my mother once said: 'I have rather a tickly cough. How about you prescribing a cough mixture for me?' Proud at being asked I prescribed, but got it wrong. The result was that during the night the cork blew out of the bottle and my mother's dressing table was covered with a sticky liquid.

I qualified at Oxford in December 1923, but have to confess that there may be some doubt about the legality of my qualification. In the anatomy exam there was a *viva* on a cadaver. The first thing I did was to scratch my hand on the cut end of a rib. By the time that this very slight injury had been washed, treated with antiseptic and covered with a dressing, the bell went and there was no time for questions. Did I pass the anatomy exam?

Qualification and first jobs

Within 24 hours of taking my degree at Oxford I went to act as a locum house physician at Paddington Green Children's Hospital. When I had been in the building for twenty minutes I was called upon to do a tracheotomy, that is, an operation to open the trachea to relieve laryngeal obstruction, usually from diphtheria. If not done promptly the patient will die. I had never seen this operation done or received any instruction in the matter. In the event I did it successfully. Why? Because of a superb casualty sister who put the patient in the proper position, with the head secured between two wooden blocks and the neck correctly extended. She then handed me the right instruments in the right order and each the right way round. She did not utter a word, but it was she who did the operation.

My father, who was a sailor and not a medical man, had the idea that it would be wise for me to be doubly qualified. Although this was nonsense, more or less to oblige him I took the Conjoint examination, that is for the Membership of the Royal College of Surgeons and Licentiate of the Royal College of Physicians, a less prestigious qualification than the Oxford degree – a waste of time and £40.

Candidates learn the result of this examination by walking down a corridor to an official who either smiles and says: 'You have passed, Sir' or looks gloomy and silently hands out a sheet of pink paper, the entry form for next time. Shortly after I took the exam a psychologically disturbed candidate, on receipt of his pink paper, drew from his pocket a drawing pin and a revolver. He pinned up the paper and fired at it. The examiners, hearing gunfire, were anxious to know what was going on. The porter entered and said in shocked tones: 'A gentleman has shot his pink paper three times, Sir'.

The culprit was brought before the examiners and immediately brandished his gun. Examiners who had seen war service took cover under the table. The man was eventually disarmed and, not surprisingly, excluded from the examination. Later, the dean of his medical school pleaded on his behalf that he had 'suffered from shell shock' in the war. The examiners relented and he did qualify. A few years later I found that he was the doctor in a ship in which my sister Hetty was sailing to South Africa. I warned her not to be ill.

Clinical appointments

My first appointments were two very minor clinical assistantships in the children's department and tuberculosis department, just to fill in time before the more serious resident posts.

Casualty officer

My first more responsible appointments were as Casualty Officer and Resident Anaesthetist. In casualty there was every kind of medical, surgical and even obstetrical emergency, and we saw a large slice of Lambeth life in the raw. Press reporters looking for a good story were sometimes a nuisance. On one occasion when we were very busy one of them wished to know the latest about 'Summer colds'. To get rid of him I said sharply: 'Summer colds occur in the summer and the others don't.' Imagine my delight when the next day's *Evening Standard* carried a large headline – *Eminent specialist explains about summer colds.*

One remembers some of the amusing incidents: an anxious young girl who said, 'Can I see the pregnant doctor?' The casualty sister was an elderly and aggressively prim woman. On another occasion a tarty Lambeth girl came to the clinic; when she was undressed for examination the casualty officer noticed that she had shaved off her pubic hair. Perhaps unwisely, he asked her why. The girl turned to Sister with a beaming smile and said: 'We girls must make ourselves attractive, mustn't we, Sister?'

Not all incidents were amusing. A man came to casualty with a small cut on his elbow, caused by another man, whom he had been abusing, throwing a piece of metal at him. This apparently trivial injury required only two stitches. The patient developed tetanus and died. His assailant appeared at the Old Bailey on a charge of manslaughter and I had to appear to give evidence. The accused's lawyer put forward the defence that his client had caused only a very minor injury and that the man's death was really caused by the incompetent or negligent doctor who had failed to give tetanus antitoxin. I felt terrible. The accused was acquitted because he had acted under great provocation. The incident happened when the injured man was working in a deep excavation, clearly in virgin soil, and it never occurred to me to think of tetanus. Presumably the bacteria were on the piece of metal.

Children with tonsillitis often have enlarged glands in the neck, but some of the weakly Lambeth children used to develop an abscess as well. Without being immodest I can say that I was good at incising them. Why? Because I did not know too much anatomy, so made a bold and adequate incision. People intimately acquainted with the complicated and important structures in the neck are terrified of putting a knife into it and so make small and inadequate incisions.

Near St Thomas's were some bad slums, and the inhabitants were a pretty rough lot. Sometimes a man would come to casualty with a foot injury. He had washed only the affected side so when the other foot was exposed for comparison it might be black. The standard excuse was: 'It's the dye off me socks, doctor.'

Our other duty was for very, very inexperienced young men to give anaesthetics for major surgery, mostly open ether – that is pouring ether on to a bit of rag held over the patient's nose and mouth. Some goes into the eye and some down the throat. It is a barbarous form of anaesthesia. When I had an ether anaesthetic it took me three days to recover. Our great ambition was to be congratulated by the surgeon for having produced 'good relaxation', which really meant that we had given far too much anaesthetic. For minor operations, such as opening an abscess, the patients were given nitrous oxide. It is a bad anaesthetic because it is now known that it acts solely by producing asphyxia and is particularly inadvisable for elderly patients. To demonstrate this fact Sir Robert Macintosh*, professor of anaesthetics at Oxford, once gave a morning's dental gases with nitrogen. No one noticed any difference.

Medical house physician

I next became house physician to Dr Charles Box. He was interested in morbid anatomy and had written a book on postmortem examination technique. His invariable greeting to his house physician was not 'Good afternoon', but 'Any postmortems?' We visited that temple of truth regularly. As a student and house physician I was on his firm for a year and during that time none of his diagnoses was ever proved wrong in the postmortem room. Although the kindest of men, his interest in morbid anatomy sometimes made him stand at the patient's bedside and describe in vivid detail what the viscera would look like in the postmortem room.

There was not much difference in the kind of diseases we saw then from those of today, except that syphilis was commoner and a diagnosis to be considered in most male patients and some female patients. Investigations were few – blood counts, blood urea and blood sugar. A request for serum potassium was regarded as eccentric. There was then no flame photometry and the chemical analysis took so long that by the time the result reached the ward the patient had either died or recovered and gone home. There were no measurements of blood hormone or drug levels. As there were no antibiotics, patients with pneumonia had to fight it out themselves, aided only by nursing care.

Our chief remedies were iron, morphia, castor oil, digitalis, potassium iodide and mercury (for syphilis), arsenic and gentian. Arsenic was used for treating incurable conditions such as lymphadenoma, and chronic arsenical poisoning was common. Gentian was an all round placebo. The modern doctor will remark that we could not have done much good. My reply will be that we did not do much harm, and that the patients were spared the alarming side effects and dangers of some modern drugs. Now there are about 3,000 drugs. The house physician, not to mention the consultant, is required to know the proprietary name, the scientific name, the indications, contraindications, dose, side effects, incompatibilities, symptoms of overdosage and the cost – that is 27,000 items of information. No wonder tired house physicians on ward rounds sometimes fall asleep at the patient's bedside.

One deplorable aspect of our therapy was purgation. When a seriously ill patient, for example with a death-threatening pneumonia, was admitted, the first thing we did was to give him a huge dose of castor oil or calomel followed by magnesium sulphate. The patient was purged, dehydrated and exhausted. In retrospect, this barbarous relic of the eighteenth century seems inexplicable, but I suppose that, as the anthropologists say, 'custom is king'. This evil practice was stopped almost immediately by a paper in The Lancet of 20 February 1937 by Leslie Witts* entitled 'Ritual Purgation in Modern Medicine'. His vivid prose style and devastating common sense make the paper a landmark. I have the impression that even today ward sisters tend to be more concerned than the physicians are about noughts for bowel movements on the patient's chart. Another change has been that if we had a patient with popliteal embolism, because the foot was cold we wrapped it up in blankets and surrounded it with hot water bottles instead of keeping it cool to delay the onset of gangrene.

The work of a house physician is hard but highly educational. He learns responsibility, a lot about acute medicine, how to deal with all kinds of people and that there are more diseases than those mentioned in the textbooks. There is great concern today about the long hours worked by junior medical staff. I suppose because we have all done it in our younger days we are less worried about their sufferings than we are about the adverse effects of lack of sleep on their mental processes and efficiency.

At St Thomas's the housemen had a few less agreeable duties. On Christmas Day tradition demanded that they donned fancy dress and were 'funny' to amuse the patients. This can be done only with the aid of a good deal of alcohol. On one occasion I hired a tramp's costume. It was so torn that in the interests of decency I had to wear a bathing dress under it. Another duty was to attend the ward maids' fancy dress dance. On one occasion I had to dance with a girl dressed as a kitchen garden. Her costume was a smelly sack covered with turnips, carrots, onions and large potatoes. Another girl was dressed in crêpe paper which despite great care soon disintegrated.

Children's house physician

In 1924 it was not obligatory to do a surgical house appointment, so I moved on to be house physician to Dr Reginald Jewesbury* in the children's ward. In fact there was no need to do house jobs at all. Students often took a basic qualification on Monday and went into full medical practice on Tuesday. Now they must do a medical and a surgical hospital job for full qualification and registration with the General Medical Council.

Work in the children's ward was harrowing. In the adult medical wards the death rate was about 10 per cent, mostly from advanced malignant disease, the troubles of old age or infections. In the children's ward the death rate was from 20 to 30 per cent. Babies with diarrhoea and vomiting died because we did not know about the electrolyte disturbances or even the need to replace salt and water. For infections such as pneumonia and meningitis there was no treatment beyond nursing care.

The childhood fevers, measles, diphtheria, whooping cough and scarlet fever, then killed about 15,000 children a year. I recently learned from the Registrar General that the present figure is 22. Now the infections can be dealt with so effectively that the commonest causes of death in children are road accidents and congenital malformations. In spite of these great and lifesaving improvements the national death rate remains the same, but people now die at the age of 80 and not at the age of 8. It was while doing the children's post that I had my introduction to euthanasia (see Chapter 13).

Membership examination

In 1926 I took the MRCP examination (a higher examination for the membership of the Royal College of Physicians of London). There were 54 candidates, of whom 27 passed. An Oxford friend and I adjourned to a nearby pub to celebrate our success. One of us remarked that if the exam became stiffer, with a higher plough rate, it would perhaps help our future careers. Little did we know what we were saying. About 30 years later when, as a College Censor, I was an examiner there were over 200 candidates – 27 got through. This was not due to higher standards, but to a different class of candidate. In the 'good old days' no one entered who was not considering a career in consulting medicine. After World War II everybody had a try. On the first occasion when I acted as an examiner, the first candidate was older than I, had dirty finger nails and an astonishing ignorance of medicine.

In the 1920s all candidates believed that in this exam costume was all-important – a dark suit for the written papers, a black jacket with pin-stripe trousers for the clinical, a morning coat for the pathology viva and, for the final viva, a morning coat, with gardenia. They also believed that during the exam the hall porter examined the hats hanging in the hall and reported the results to the Censors' Board. If your hat came from Lock's of St James's Street (hatters to the Duke of Wellington) your chances were much better than if it came from Dunn's (hatters to the common man). Today, sartorial elegance counts less than clean finger nails and civility to the patients.

Medical registrar

In 1926 I was appointed as medical registrar, not 'a' medical registrar but 'the' medical registrar. In this large teaching hospital there were three registrars, one for medicine, one for surgery and one for obstetrics and gynaecology. There are now dozens of them.

The title 'Registrar' may sound curious to some people for a rank in the medical hierarchy. Its origin is that our chief work was registering the patients' notes. We spent most of the day at a desk writing out an index card for each patient and collecting data. At the end of the year we pre-pared an immense statistical report, with the patients divided into age groups, comments on changes in disease, changes in treatment and accounts of unusual and interesting cases. This was published. Standing in for the senior staff when they were on holiday was a relatively minor part of our duties.

Another function was sometimes to deputize for one of the physicians, Sir Maurice Cassidy*, in his capacity as Chief Medical Officer to the Metropolitan Police. On the first occasion I made my way to the police medical department on the Embankment. I entered, a tall young man looking rather lost, and was immediately told by an inspector to 'Stand over there. Don't talk.' It was obviously no good arguing, so I nearly became a policeman but was rescued by another inspector who knew me.

During my term as registrar there occurred Britain's only General

Strike, in support of the miners' strike. By modern standards it was a peaceful affair, with no violence, no cars turned over, no firearms and no petrol bombs. There was one stab wound in London. As there was no public transport and I lived in Hampstead I borrowed a car, but on the first day had a collision and the car was a write-off. This serious situation was solved by a kind invitation from the treasurer of the hospital, Sir Arthur Stanley*, to stay in his official residence in the hospital where he lived in considerable style. His butler (or was it his valet?) unpacked my torn pyjamas, undarned socks and tatty underwear.

The junior medical staff were urged to become special constables. I was late in applying and found that only a few uniforms were left. The only jacket of my size was full of moth holes, but I had to have it. There were no uniform trousers left, so I wore a pair of my own, dark blue, but unfortunately with a smart pin stripe. There were no caps, so I bought a chauffeur's cap in the New Cut and fitted on the constabulary badge. To make matters worse, at Sir Arthur Stanley's luncheon table each day I sat next to another guest, Sir Percy Laurie, who was the commander of the Metropolitan Mounted Police and, of course, an immaculate cavalryman. We must have made a bizarre contrast.

After two or three days the special constabulary were told that they were about to go on a dangerous mission. Married men need not go. Greatcoats must be worn with the collars turned up to protect against flying glass. We were woken at four in the morning and given an unusually good breakfast. A fleet of sports cars appeared and by six o'clock we were roaring through the City of London at 60 miles an hour to Thameshaven, a large petrol depôt east of London. It was rumoured that the strikers would prevent petrol leaving the depôt and might even sabotage the plant. On arrival we confronted the strikers. It is true that two men did shout some rude words from a distance, but the main body of strikers and the specials adjourned to a neighbouring pub, happily drinking beer and playing darts together. So ended the Battle of Thameshaven.

The St Thomas's specials also had a section of shock troops, mostly recruited from the rugger club. They were told to go to a pub in South London where subversive elements were plotting the overthrow of the State, and to eject them. This they did with skill and some violence. Unfortunately their map reading was not good and it was not only the wrong pub but it contained a Labour Member of Parliament. There were questions in the House. The General Strike lasted about nine days.

General practice and job-hunting

For my fortnight's holiday I thought that I would have a try at general practice so I went to do a locum in a poor area near Chatham. The doctor left me a list of patients with name and diagnosis, but did not say whether man, woman or child. His secretary/chauffeuse drove me round. We reached the first patient. This was an important moment in my career – my first patient outside a hospital. Full of Oslerian ideals, I entered the house from bright sunlight to find it in complete darkness. When I had become dark-adapted I discerned a cot. In it was a child. The mother did not say anything, and I eventually realized that the child was dead. I could not give a death certificate but only express my sympathy. I thought, what a start to private practice. The doctor looked in next day to give the certificate.

Next, I went to see a woman in a bed in the corner of a very dark room. I had been taught that it was important to examine the patient in a good light, so I began to pull the bed towards the window. As a result I dislodged the pile of bricks on which one corner was resting and the whole bed collapsed in pieces. Worse was to follow. I went to see a woman whom my employer had been unable to diagnose, and I was no wiser. Her husband, a large and aggressive man, manoeuvred me into a corner of the room and with his face six inches from mine shouted: 'Has my wife got cancer?' I managed to escape by talking hard and enveloping him in a haze of words.

The next patient was an elderly lady with a large rodent ulcer on the nose, always kept covered with a dressing. My instructions here were pre-cise – 'Make polite conversation on any topics until you are offered a whisky and soda. This you may accept or decline as you please, but it indicates that the visit is over. On no account ask to see the ulcer', which was of course the reason for the visit.

I had asked my employer if there was any midwifery. He replied that there was only one case, and that not likely to happen for some weeks. I said: 'You can never tell', and asked where the midwifery bag was. He showed me. Needless to say, a few days later an anxious husband appeared in the middle of the night and said that his wife was in labour. Patting myself on my back for my foresight, I picked up the midwifery bag and followed him. On arrival at the house, I agreed with his diagnosis, and wondered what to do next, so I opened the bag. It sounds incredible, but is the absolute truth, that the bag contained only one blade of the obstetrical forceps, a syringe without a plunger, a piece of string and an empty cigarette box. I told the husband that I had to go back to the surgery to fetch some special apparatus. I found the other blade of the forceps in the garage where, I suspect, the doctor had been changing a tyre with it. I collected a few obvious necessaries. When I returned to the house, the mother had in her arms a baby which had been delivered by the nurse. The parents were not at all pleased with me but little did they know how lucky they were. As this was the only midwifery case in my whole medical career, I have a good record – no maternal mortality or morbidity, no fetal mortality or morbidity, which is more than most obstetricians can say.

It was a dispensing practice and the dispensary was in a tumbledown greenhouse. All the bottles were labelled, not with the name of the contents but with the name of the condition which they were supposed to cure – *Mist. pro tussis, Mist. pro backache,* etc. They were all concentrated preparations so the bottles required the addition of *Aqua purissima fontis;* in addition, they were mostly colourless, so one had to add one of three dyes, red, green or orange, and not forget to enter in the day book the colour of that patient's bottle of medicine. There was also a collection of labels to be stuck on the bills that were sent out to the patients, some polite, some less polite and some threatening litigation. A fortnight's experience of this general practice convinced me that it was all much too difficult and that I had better aim for something simple and straightforward like consulting medicine.

Resident assistant physician

My next appointment was as Resident Assistant Physician (RAP). The holder of this post was the senior resident, had general supervision of the medical beds, had some duties with admissions, discharges and waiting lists (then mercifully short) and saw all medical emergencies. In those days he also had another, but archaic duty. When a patient was discharged from the hospital the RAP had to sign the admission sheet and inscribe a large letter P. This indicated that the patient had been 'Presented' to the governors to give thanks for his treatment.

It was a very whole-time job. I went for weeks and even months at a time without ever leaving the hospital. The post is now carried out by registrars in turn who live in the hospital for a week at a time. My opposite number was the Resident Assistant Surgeon (RAS), who did all the emergency surgery that occurred out of office hours. Not long before our reign, for nocturnal emergencies the practice had been for the RAS to write a short account of the patient and his diagnosis and give it to a porter, who took a hansom cab and went clop, clop, clop up to Harley Street to the surgeon on duty. He would glance at the note and write at the bottom: 'Please carry on.' The cab went clop, clop back to the hospital. The RAS just had to get on with it in our day .

There was a strict and interesting rule that all acute abdominal emergencies had to be seen by a physician, because there are a few medical conditions, such as spontaneous pneumothorax or tabetic crisis, that can mimic surgical conditions. The reason for this rule was that although the surgeons were skilful cutters they were not then the thoughtful diagnosticians of today. It was a fascinating experience for a physician to see several acute abdomens a day. My colleague and I were keen young men and in these cases wrote down what we thought the diagnosis would be to compare it with the actual result. We got about 75 per cent correct. We then found that about 75 per cent of acute abdomens were due to appendicitis, so anyone who shuts his eyes and says 'appendicitis' does just as well as the person who tries to sort out perforated gastric ulcer, appendicitis, cholecystitis, and intestinal obstruction.

The great London flood occurred during my term of office. An unusually high tide, a strong wind in the wrong direction and the fact that London is slowly sinking, caused the Thames to overflow the parapets of the Embankment. A large area of central London was under water. Fourteen people living in basements were drowned in their beds. I have a vivid recollection of the basement of the hospital at three o'clock in the morning. I was standing in a foot of rising water begging the London Fire Brigade to get on with the pumping before the water reached the electrics and put the hospital out of action. They just succeeded. As an immediate remedy the authorities raised the parapets of the Embankment a few inches. Many years later they erected the Thames Barrier.

St Thomas's was old fashioned in that the physicians had beds but did not do outpatients, and the assistant physicians did outpatients but had no beds. This gave rise to the ridiculous situations that patients were discharged from hospital to be followed up by someone who had never seen them before, and that when an interesting problem appeared in outpatients the patient would be admitted under the care of somebody else and the assistant physician might never see that patient again. Another unsatisfactory practice was that shortly before an outpatient clinic the senior medical casualty officer (a sort of registrar) quickly looked through the mass of patients and selected six or eight 'good teaching cases', that is patients with easily diagnosable textbook diseases – mitral stenosis, hyperthyroidism, diabetes or disseminated sclerosis. This enabled the outpatient physician to give a dazzling display of confident and accurate diagnosis, but it made the students think that all patients were like that, which they certainly are not. Meanwhile the real puzzles that required the advice of an experienced physician were seen by the back room boy.

After a year, in 1928, I left to get married and, perhaps rashly, went on my honeymoon with no job. A fortnight later we received a telegram which said that I had been appointed as first assistant on the professorial medical unit.

First assistant on professorial medical unit

Professorial medical units had their origin in the United States of America. In 1910 Dr Abraham Flexner* wrote a book, *Medical Education in the United States and Canada*. The medical schools were numerous, some distinguished and some of a very low standard. Applicants for admission to a medical school had to produce evidence of 'general education' in the form of an arts degree. These too were of variable standards. One school accepted a student whose evidence of general education was graduation in beekeeping, punctuation and jujitsu.

In 1912 Flexner wrote another book, *Medical Education in Europe*, in which he criticized the British system, saying that we produced good doctors not because of it but in spite of it. Clinical teaching was done by the honorary staffs, practically unpaid both for their clinical work and for their teaching, who naturally had to spend much of their time earning their livings in private practice. Many had long since lost any interest in the laboratory or the scientific aspects of medicine. Flexner gave evidence before the Haldane* Commission on London University (1910-1913). He advocated salaried and nearly whole-time teachers, and instanced the success of this system at Johns Hopkins University and Berlin University. He was strongly supported by Sir William Osler.

The first such unit in London was formed in 1918 at St Bartholomew's Hospital, with Sir Archibald Garrod as professor. As the author of *Inborn Errors of Metabolism* in 1909, he was a distinguished investigator. St Thomas's followed suit in 1919. The first professor was Hugh Maclean*, an Aberdonian especially interested in the chemical aspects of medicine, such as gastric acidity and diabetes. The medical unit had well-equipped laboratories, but in 1922 the discovery of insulin caused remarkable changes. Maclean, an ambitious man, was not going to be left out of the race to make this important new medicament. In a moment all the electric apparatus was swept away and replaced by mincing machines and vats. He succeeded.

Later, when I came on the unit, my duties were to help with the care of our 60 beds, to teach students and to try to do research. Maclean took the view that as gastric ulcers were often associated with high gastric acidity the treatment should be with alkalis, and in large doses. Some patients developed alkalosis and became very ill. I was interested in this condition and later wrote a thesis on it for the Oxford DM degree. We also had special outpatient clinics for diabetes and for gastric and duodenal ulcers. The contrast was striking. The diabetics were always cheerful; the ulcer patients invariably miserable.

I have one embarrassing recollection. The diabetic clinic was small and lasted from two o'clock until about four. On one occasion when it was over I returned to the laboratory and continued my research. I was just about to go home at seven o'clock, three hours later, when a diabetic patient who had been forgotten put his head round the door and said in unemotional tones: 'Shall I be seen soon, doctor ?' I was horrified, but the patient was not. He just assumed that one was often kept waiting for three hours at medical clinics. I sent him home in a taxi.

Deputy Director

Later that year I was promoted to deputy director of the unit, whereupon the professor had a serious illness and was out of action for the following year. I did my best to run the unit, and it was a valuable experience. In 1931 it looked as if Maclean might never come back and the chair was filled by Dr O.L.V.S. de Wesselow*.

Finale at St Thomas's

I then began to realize that it was about time I obtained a permanent appointment somewhere. Shortly after, there occurred a vacancy on the staff of St Thomas's, for which I applied. The practice was for applicants to call on all members of the senior staff, presumably to make themselves known. I had by then worked in the hospital for ten years. I was told that I was not likely to be elected, but that it was wise to show the flag. Some months later there was another vacancy and I applied again. I repeated my round of calls and was told by a number of people that I was likely to be elected. I thought that things were looking up. I was not elected. This was a shattering blow. My little world fell in pieces.

I now realise that far from a disaster it was a singular stroke of good fortune. Had I been elected it would have been a real disaster. I had no money. I did not even possess a motor car. I could not have afforded rooms in Harley Street or kept up with the social striving then prevalent in London consulting practice. An example of this affectation of superiority was displayed by the wife of a St Thomas's physician who once said to my wife: 'Of course I have the largest drawing room in Wimpole Street.'

Perhaps I may add that my rejection was not entirely due to my shortcomings, but also to the fact that the hospital's only neurologist, Dr James Birley*, had died and had to be replaced by another neurologist, so Jack Elkington* was elected. I continued job hunting, with two unsuccessful attempts at University College Hospital. At one of these I was interviewed by Sir Thomas Lewis* and had a delightful afternoon helping him with an experiment. Providentially there then occurred a vacancy at Oxford and I applied. There was no interview – it was all done by post.

In December 1932 I developed pneumonia, I have to confess after a very late party at a night club. I was admitted to St Thomas's seriously ill, with a high temperature for 12 days. There was no nonsense about antibiotics, and at one period my wife was advised to spend the night at the hospital 'in case anything happened'. I then heard that I had been appointed as an assistant physician to the Radcliffe Infirmary, and received a charming note of congratulation from Sir Charles Sherrington*. The Governors of the St Thomas's Medical School very kindly, in appreciation of my efforts on the unit, gave me a cheque for £50, then a substantial sum.

Working at Oxford

While I was convalescent my wife and her father made several expeditions to Oxford to look for a house. After my recovery my Oxford colleague Fred Hobson* asked when I could come to Oxford, because in addition to his own work he was doing that of the late William Collier*, whom I was replacing. I would obviously need a car. As I was hard up I started by walking down Great Portland Street in London, then a centre of the second-hand car market, but the salesmen were such a collection of smooth deceivers that I decided that it would have to be a new car. I bought a brand new Morris 10 which cost £189-10-0. I saw it still in use 25 years later.

On March 21st 1933 I moved into lodgings in Oxford while our house was being decorated, and started work at the Radcliffe Infirmary. On May 2nd we moved into our new house at 123 Woodstock Road in North Oxford, a pleasant Victorian semi-detached mansion built about

Our new house at 123 Woodstock Road in North Oxford

1880 with four reception rooms, eight bedrooms, two bathrooms and a basement with extensive catacombs, the whole covering about one third of an acre. The front garden had a gravelled path round a small circular rosebed and several tatty little flower beds at the sides.

In about 1880 the house had been sold by auction and we had among the documents of the house a notice of the sale. It was a masterpiece of the house agent's art and included 'The house is approached by a handsome carriage sweep through spacious pleasure gardens.' We had bought the last 22 years of a 50-year leasehold. That seemed quite a long time but was over remarkably quickly.

As we were hard up we thought that it would be a good idea if we had a resident patient – an amiable, well-to-do, elderly lady with some harmless mental disorder. One of my St Thomas's friends had managed this with great success. So just after coming out of hospital I called on Henry Yellowlees*, the psychiatrist of St Thomas's. Perhaps unwisely, I combined this visit with returning a shotgun that I had borrowed. The arrival on his doorstep of a haggard-looking young man carrying a gun made the staff look anxious. Yellowlees could not help and we never got our resident patient.

We found Oxford most friendly and hospitable and were extensively entertained. After a few months we thought that we ought to give some return hospitality, so we gave a dinner party for eight people, most of them old enough to be our parents. It was a serious affair, with the men in tails, with white ties, and the ladies in full evening dress.

We hired a waitress. There were two of these admirable women, Miss Green and Miss Williamson, and we always ensured that one of them could come before we ever thought of asking any guests. One or other would arrive about 5 o'clock in a black dress, carrying a small parcel, which contained a white pinafore and her favourite carving knife. She would set the table and, if time permitted, help to put the children to bed. At dinner she carved, waited at table and afterwards washed up, all for a very small fee. One or other of them was seen at most dinner parties and they knew the guests. They might say 'You will like this, Dr X', or 'This is not on your diet, Mrs Y'. I had some of those enormous brandy goblets of which I was very proud, but Miss Green said: 'The Regius Professor of Civil Law has some larger than that.'

At this first dinner party we thought carefully about the menu. As it was a hot summer we decided to start with cold consommé. We had an inexperienced cook. When the soup would not set she added a lot of gelatin. When it was served it looked good and smelt good but had the consistency of a motor tyre. We all had to prise a piece of soup off and chew it for what seemed an eternity. Nowadays this sort of incident would be thought amusing, but not in 1933. Fortunately, the rest of the dinner went better.

My work at the Infirmary was chiefly two outpatient clinics a week. This sounds easy, but I was in fact busy because it was the practice then for newly-appointed consultants to call on all their consultant colleagues. This was an agreeable duty except for my visit to the superintendent of the local mental hospital. In parking my car I inadvertently backed into one of those metal hoops placed to stop people walking on the lawns. There was a noise as if I had backed into several bicycles. I tried to move my car forward but it remained stationary. The answer was that I had also backed on to a little stone post on which the car's back axle was now resting. A posse of ambulant patients had to be summoned to lift my car off the post.

The Regius Professor of Medicine was Sir Farquhar Buzzard, Bt*, a former physician to St Thomas's Hospital and physician to King George V. He had been, and still was, a noted athlete, an Oxford soccer blue, and had played for the Corinthians and Casuals. When over 60 he would play six sets of tennis and then beat at squash a man half his own age. Good amateur players were sometimes allowed to appear with professional teams. There was a famous occasion when Buzzard turned out, I think for Tottenham Hotspur. Although quite unknown to the crowd, every time he kicked the ball there was applause and when he scored a goal there were loud cheers. He was naturally surprised at all this until he saw the card of the match, where his name had been spelt with two gs instead of two zs. He was a good person to work with and I got on well with him.

My stipend as assistant physician was nil, but I did receive £25 a year for looking after the notes and preparing a small annual report. I then had the good fortune to be appointed the first May Reader in Medicine, with a stipend of £320 a year, and assistant to the Regius Professor of Medicine at £150 a year. The founder of the readership, Miss Harriet May, wished the holder to study deafness. In those days there were only two kinds of deafness – wax in the ears, which was curable, and all the other kinds, which were not.

Sir Farquhar Buzzard was keen to form links or bridges between the preclinical and clinical parts of the medical school. He therefore suggested that I should give two lecture-demonstrations a week on patients in the hospital to the students working in the anatomy and physiology departments. I had the run of the hospital wards, medical and surgical, and took trouble to find patients with conditions related to what my audience was studying in the preclinical departments. The demonstrations proved remarkably popular because it was the first time that these students had ever been in a hospital or seen a real patient. It helped them to understand that what they were doing in the pre-clinical departments had some bearing on the diagnosis and treatment of patients.

On several occasions I have met some of these students, perhaps twenty years later, and they have remarked on 'the case of so-and-so that you showed us in 1937.' I recently had some correspondence with a former pupil, now a distinguished pathologist. At the end of his letter he wrote: 'I am still grateful for the child recovering from polio and the nun with pernicious anaemia that you showed us in 1942.' I then realized that this was half a century before.

Despite the general success of these lecture-demonstrations there was one disaster. I planned a talk on blood groups and blood transfusion. As one of my patients was needing a transfusion I took the class (mercifully small as it was the last lecture of the term) to the ward. I said my piece and all went well until the blood was produced. A large athletic-looking student fainted and was immediately followed by five other young men. None of the girls fainted. The place looked like a battlefield. The patient, white as a sheet, roared with laughter and obviously thought that it was the best entertainment and the funniest thing he had ever seen.

On another occasion I was giving a lecture on a patient with mitral stenosis. She suddenly began to be sick, so I held a porringer in front of her. This made a member of the audience faint and I had to catch the vomit, resuscitate the fainter, and give a lecture at the same time. It can be done, but is difficult. I did not use the ward technique again.

It was clear that my main source of income would have to be private practice. I had heard gloomy tales of eminent physicians who had made only a few guineas in their first year. I did make £400, which with the other sources mentioned above amounted to £900, a trivial sum nowadays, but in 1933 a modest but reasonable income. After all, as deputy director of the medical unit at St Thomas's I had lived, with a wife and child, on £450 a year. It does not sound much, but we lived comfortably, went to the theatre, drank gin, entertained, had holidays and were never in debt.

In Oxford the fee for a consultation in my early days was two guineas for a working-class patient and three guineas for a grander patient. For distances it was about a guinea a mile. The charging of fees has always been a source of difficulty and embarrassment to me and I have never enjoyed it. On the one hand, I have been humiliated by a patient who said: 'If that is all you charge you cannot be very distinguished'; on the other hand, I have sometimes felt that I was causing serious financial embarrassment to poor people. There was one dreadful occasion when I was asked to see a patient in a slum. The house was dirty, with holes

The fee for a consultation in my early days was two guineas for a working class patient and three guineas for a grander patient

in the few carpets and every indication of poverty. I said to the general practitioner: 'I can't possibly charge these people a fee.' He replied: 'Don't be deceived. They can well afford to pay your usual fee.' So I sent an account for a few guineas. The fee was paid in cash, mostly small change, with an accompanying dirty piece of paper listing all the neighbours, family and friends who had contributed. On the other hand, an unwashed gipsy produced the largest bundle of £20 notes I have ever seen. Appearances are often deceptive. It turned out that an opulent-looking patient with a large Rolls-Royce could not read or write.

Before World War II, when a pound was worth a pound, a surgical colleague and I received an anonymous gift of £2,000 in notes from a hospital patient, accompanied by a letter full of spelling mistakes and signed only with 'Yours turly' and initials. We consulted the police and hospital authorities and were told to keep it.

The life of a physician is materially influenced by his wife and by his secretary. My wife, Vera, although she came from a Christian Science family, soon adapted to medicine. One of her many agreeable traits was that if she saw a lame duck or someone in trouble she had a compulsion to help them. In consequence, on a number of occasions the relatives of a seriously-ill patient, hospital or private, who happened to live a long way from Oxford would be invited to stay with us until the danger was over. I never attempted to teach her medicine, but she had the built-in ability to diagnose adenoids from a distance of 100 yards. She also learnt by observation to diagnose myxoedema.

I cannot remember all my private secretaries but I must have had eight or ten over the years. The first was a pleasant and competent girl, but she smelt. The cause turned out to be due to sweating with a temperature of 102°. The poor girl later died of Hodgkin's disease. I have had the best secretary in the world and also the worst. The former, whose salary was £2 a week, was a remarkable girl. I would say to her: 'Audrey, tell him I don't want to do it and tell him not to be silly'. She would produce a letter exactly word for word what I would have said. The worst one got me into trouble. I was allowed to take books out of the Radcliffe Science Library, which is a branch of the Bodleian Library. I once asked her to take some books back to the Science Library. Instead, she posted them to the Royal Society of Medicine in London. About six months later they were sent back to Bodley, who were not at all pleased. At the Radcliffe Infirmary I had as my secretary the faithful Kathy Middleton for many years. Once when she was on holiday I had a remarkable locum. She took my letters down in shorthand and they were faultless. Just before she left she owned up that she did not know shorthand, but made nonsensical squiggly marks in her notebook and committed the material to memory. She never made a mistake. On another occasion I borrowed a secretary from a colleague. I started to dictate a letter with the words 'I saw this young woman . . .' I asked her to read it back. Without batting an eyelid she read 'I saw this damned woman . . .' To avoid this sort of unpleasant blunder I have never sent a letter out without having read it and signed it myself.

I had the good fortune to be elected a member of the Senior Common Room at Jesus College, where I had been an undergraduate. There were then only about ten Fellows. One was the Jesus Professor of Celtic, a learned Scotsman who did not like lecturing to undergraduates. He was compelled by statute to announce his lectures, which he did on Saturday at 3.30 pm in some inaccessible place, which ensured that nobody turned up. This worked well for some years, but when a fellow of Magdalen College wished to study some documents in Old Irish the professor had to lecture. This caused much merriment in college. I asked him one day how his audience was doing. He replied: 'Very badly. It went beagling last Saturday.'

As well as my hospital work and private practice, as a Reader I was expected to do research. I started by trying to continue work that I had done at St Thomas's. I had published a paper in the *Quarterly Journal of Medicine* on the damaging effects of alkalosis on the kidney and one on calcification of the kidneys in pyloric stenosis, also presumed to be related to alkalosis. I therefore thought of trying the effects of hyperventilation on the kidneys. I acquired a vivisection licence and worked on decerebrate cats. I had no access to micromethods of blood analysis, so had to take relatively large amounts of blood for analysis. As a result the cats never lived long enough for there to be any effects of hyperventilation on the kidney, so I gave up the project. I then worked with J. G. Priestly, an Oxford physiologist, on measurement of the output of the heart by inhaling acetylene. Not long before, two Danish physiologists had died while doing similar work from toxic impurities in the acetylene. In order to avoid this risk, we rigged up a long chain of washbottles, each designed to remove a particular poison. We found that the gas from the final washbottle contained no acetylene but still had its characteristic smell. We then found that cylinders of pure acetylene could be obtained. An unimportant paper resulted.

Another project arose when we had patients on anticoagulants which had to be injected every few hours, including the middle of the night. This was extremely unpleasant for the patients, not to mention the doctors. We thought that if we gave a larger dose dissolved in some inert menstruum, it would be absorbed slowly and obviate night injections. Before trying it on a patient we tried it on a medical student. The only effect was to produce an enormous haematoma and make the young man really ill. We thought that he should go home to convalesce. When his father, an eminent physician, came to collect him, we foresaw a possibly painful interview. All his father said was: 'When do you want him back for the next experiment?' In my experience successful research requires not only special intellectual gifts but a good deal of luck.

Of all my activities one that I specially enjoyed was doing outpatients. It was almost the only truly clinical medicine that I did. A patient would complain of certain symptoms, I would take a history, make a physical examination and try to arrive at the diagnosis without any investigations. In the wards, efficient young men would rush up and tell me all about the electrocardiogram and the serum potassium. That's not real medicine.

On one occasion an old Oxfordshire ploughman came to the clinic. I took my usual careful history. When I came to examine him I found that he had a laparotomy scar. I said: 'I see that you have had an operation. What was that for?' He replied 'Oi don't know. When they gets insoide, they helps themselves.'

The next event of interest was in 1935 when I was elected a Fellow of the Royal College of Physicians of London. This was a pleasant and unexpected surprise. The news made me blush – for the first and last time in my life. There were about thirty new Fellows, in contrast to the hundreds of today. I was then asked to visit the Horton General Hospital at Banbury twice a month and the Moreton-in-Marsh Hospital once a month. At Banbury many of the house officers were Indians, so at lunch there was always curry, plus a large selection of chutneys and other condiments. I once helped myself to a chutney, but it turned out to be only chillis. After choking, I became red in the face with tears running down my cheeks. One of my consultant colleagues came in to see me, looked embarrassed, and left thinking that I was having a psychological crisis.

In 1934 it had been announced that the annual meeting of the British Medical Association would be held in Oxford in 1936, with Sir Farquhar Buzzard as president, Fred Hobson as general secretary, and myself as science secretary. I had never been to an annual meeting and thought that it would be wise to try to find out something about it. In 1934 the meeting was held in Bournemouth, where my father and sister lived, so I repaired there.

I made myself known to the harassed secretary and learnt that as well as the lectures, demonstrations and discussions, which are the main reasons for the meeting, a dinner, a dance and other social functions had been laid on. In addition, there was provision for a variety of recreations, including golf, tennis, bowls, skating and sailing. On the first day of the meeting a doctor called at the office and asked if there was any chance of some church bell ringing. We took this to heart and at our meeting two

Life in Oxford was pleasant

35

years later my very efficient colleague Fred Hobson laid on all the usual recreations, plus church bell ringing. On the first day of our meeting a doctor came into the office and asked if there was any chance of meeting some fellow stamp collectors.

Apart from Fred Hobson's problems, the BMA meeting seemed to be a success. There were two notable features. One was the announcement of Lord Nuffield's* Benefaction to the University. The other was that immediately after the President's address in the Sheldonian Theatre, which was crammed to capacity, it was revealed that the building, designed by Wren*, was in a dangerous state and likely to collapse at any moment. The two upper floors, entirely of wood, were approached by two narrow staircases, a terrible fire hazard. Later the Sheldonian was made safe by the architect Mr Fielding Dodd, a good friend of ours. Dodd built two ferroconcrete staircases, skilfully disguised by panelling. The two upper floors were supported by columns which were just tree trunks. Each now has a three-inch steel stanchion inside.

Life in Oxford was pleasant, with interesting work, college life, good friends, plenty of music and the Cotswolds and Stratford-upon-Avon nearby. We lived in what would nowadays be regarded as considerable comfort. We had a cook, a house parlourmaid, a children's nurse, a girl as general factotum, a secretary and a gardener. On one occasion when we acquired a new cook my wife said to her: 'We'll have a steamed pudding for lunch. The girl's face fell and she said: 'I only do *plain* cooking – tinned fruit and that.'

Every morning my wife sat down and wrote out three menus, one for the dining room, one for the nursery and one for the kitchen. On one occasion, having nothing else to do, we started counting up the number of persons that we had employed in the previous thirty years, When we got to about 40 we tired of the exercise. Secretaries came and went. My secretary always kept a petty cash book. On one occasion I happened to glance at it and found that it had been raided by my wife. The last two entries read:

Turbot 4s 6d

Salvation Army Self Denial Week 2s 6d

In 1938 I was promoted to full physician. The only practical difference was that my stipend went down from £25 to £22 6s 8d per annum, from an 18th century endowment.

Of course, there were sometimes bad moments and nobody can fail to be moved by pain, suffering, death and bereavement. There was a dreadful occasion when a boy was admitted under my care. At first we could not make head or tail of his condition, but eventually found what looked like an abscess of the spine. He was transferred to the orthopaedic surgeons, who operated but could find nothing. The boy died and even the post mortem examination did not reveal the cause of death. The boy's parents were not only upset but furious and said that he had been neglected and not even been seen by a doctor. This was not true. I had seen him myself three times each day and he had been seen by eleven doctors in all. The father was an employee of a friend of mine, who wrote to me suggesting that it might calm things down if I interviewed the parents. This I would gladly have done, but the Medical Defence Union, to whom I had already written, strongly advised me not to. Instead they sent a letter for me to send to the parents. It seemed to me a most inappropriate document. It was harsh in tone and contained both technical terms and Latin phrases. After further correspondence with the union I translated it into plain English and sent it.

To change to a more cheerful subject – the British have a great liking for celebrating centenaries, although this is a relatively modern practice and seldom occurred until the 19th century. Between 1964 and 1978 I took part in six centenaries, some medical, some not. The first was the 700th anniversary of the foundation of Merton College in 1264. There was a good deal of eating, drinking and speechmaking and some glorious fireworks. At the time I was a member of the wine committee and remember ordering 1,200 bottles of champagne.

In 1968 was the 450th anniversary of the foundation of the Royal College of Physicians of London in 1518. Vera and I spent a whole week in London staying in style in the Chandos Suite of the Royal Society of Medicine. There were a church service, a reception, dinners, the Harveian Oration and other lectures (one by me on The College and Europe).

Next came the bicentenary of the Radcliffe Infirmary in 1970. There were a church service, a ball at Blenheim Palace, the planting of a hippocratic plane tree, a party at Blackwell's*, a luncheon, a dinner and a performance of Handel's *Jephtha* in the Sheldonian Theatre.

In 1971 Jesus College celebrated the 400th anniversary of its foundation with a church service and a gaudy.

In 1978 was the 400th anniversary of the birth of William Harvey*, celebrated at the Royal College of Physicians of London and at Merton College, where he was for a time Warden. There were lectures and a dinner. I conducted a party from the College of Physicians round Merton.

One feature common to all centenary celebrations is an appeal for funds. Under the influence of a good dinner, alcohol and sentiment one is apt to sign a four-year covenant. It is forgotten until one notices a much depleted bank balance.

The last celebration is not medical, but is included because it was such an enjoyable occasion. In 1935 we celebrated the 250th anniversary of the births of J. S. Bach and G. F. Handel in 1685 and had a wonderful fortnight of their music. The organisers of the festival had managed to borrow the original score of Handel's *Messiah* from the Royal Library at Windsor and were anxious to obtain that of Bach's *B minor Mass* from a library in Berlin. The Bach manuscript was so precious that it could not be allowed to leave the building. The organisers persevered, and by luring the Herr Direktor of the Berlin Library with the promise of an honorary degree, induced him to bring the manuscript himself. After the end of the festival the Herr Direktor departed with the precious score but, perhaps as the result of a rather good dinner, left it in the train to London. Fortunately a porter at Paddington found it and took it to the Lost Property Office.

CHAPTER SIX

Lord Nuffield's Benefaction

Lord Nuffield's Benefaction of 1936 had its roots in the 1920s; its chief begetters were Sir Farquhar Buzzard and Mr (later Sir) Hugh Cairns*. In 1923 the Rockefeller* Foundation gave Oxford University the then very large sum of £75,000 to build a biochemistry laboratory. Abraham Flexner, of the Foundation, was much impressed by the distinction of the Oxford pre-clinical departments and felt that an Institute of Clinical Research would be a valuable addition to the medical school. In 1927 the Foundation made such a proposal to the University but it was not so much turned down as simply ignored. It came in the middle of the long vacation when nobody who mattered was about, and the University then took very little interest in medical affairs.

In the following year the Foundation tried again, this time approaching the Minister of Health, Neville Chamberlain*. He was interested and set up a committee of eminent clinicians to advise on the project, including Lord Dawson of Penn*, Lord Moynihan*, Sir Humphry Rolleston* and Sir Farquhar Buzzard. There was no consultation with London University or the Medical Research Council. This plan failed too, but it is probable that it sowed the seed for the idea of what is now the Royal Postgraduate Medical School which was opened in 1935, seven years later.

Buzzard, who had been on Chamberlain's committee, was shocked at this good money running to waste, and when he took up the office of Regius Professor of Medicine at Oxford in 1928 was determined that it should never happen again.

Here William Morris, later Lord Nuffield*, comes on the scene. Before World War I he had premises in Longwall Street, Oxford, a stone's throw from my present house, where he sold and repaired bicycles. In addition, he made a few motor-cars. After the war the car business boomed and he became a millionaire. As a young man he had wished to study medicine but could not afford to do so. When he became rich he indulged his interest by making generous gifts to Guy's and St Thomas's hospitals, and later to Oxford. As Malcolm Macdonald*, when Minister of Health, said: 'How fortunate for medicine it was that Nuffield had not become a doctor.' Nuffield maintained a keen interest in medicine all his life, and in his bedroom had a shelf of medical books for nocturnal reading. At one time he was troubled by insomnia, which was cured by reading the *British Pharmacopoeia*. There can be few more effective books for this purpose. As a millionaire he had an enormous postbag. Every charity, every sponger and many lunatics wrote to him. It took two secretaries to deal with his mail. Most letters went into the wastepaper basket, some had a formal reply and a few reached his desk.

Nuffield was made Vice-President of the Radcliffe Infirmary and it did not take Buzzard long to persuade him to buy the Radcliffe Observatory which is immediately adjacent to the Infirmary. The observers had said that they could not see the stars clearly because it was too misty in Oxford, although it apparently took them 200 years to find this out. The observatory was not a university department so the astronomical work was removed to South Africa. It seems a leisurely job being an astronomer: I was told that it took two years to build the new observatory, two more years to construct the telescopes and other apparatus and a further two years for the instruments to settle down.

Of the large Radcliffe Observatory area, about half went to the Infirmary, which greatly enlarged its site, and the other half, with the building, to the University on condition that within five years a scheme for medical research should be formulated. This scheme envisaged that the Observatory building would accommodate a ward of six to eight beds, a laboratory, and offices. I happened to be on the committee that examined the building and the project. It was at once obvious that the building was quite unsuitable for a ward. In the event the Observatory was used for X-ray cinematography and experimental therapeutics, and later became the Nuffield Institute for Medical Research. This institution later moved to Headington and the Observatory now houses Green College.

Lord Nuffield was impervious to any direct request for money, however deserving the cause. There was a special technique for arousing his interest, and it was widely believed that this involved playing golf at Huntercombe, about fifteen miles south-east of Oxford. Incidentally, when his wife applied to join the golf club and was blackballed because her husband was 'in trade', his Lordship's riposte was to buy the establishment and give it to his wife for a birthday present. Buzzard had carefully studied the technique of Nuffield management.

Now Hugh Cairns comes on the scene. He was an Australian Rhodes scholar who, after three years' war service in the Australian Army Medical Corps, came up to Balliol in 1920. He did not take a degree but did some surgical work at the Radcliffe Infirmary, gained a rowing blue and married one of the daughters of the Master of his College. He was then appointed a surgeon to the London Hospital and went to the United States to work with Harvey Cushing*, which hooked him on neurosurgery. On his return he started a neurosurgical unit, the first of its kind in London, with the aid of Rockefeller funds. He had little space and poor facilities, which led him to think what a good idea it would be to transfer his unit to Oxford. He then broadened this idea to include a high-quality clinical research school. In 1935 he wrote to Buzzard about this plan and received a sympathetic response.

Buzzard was wise and a man of affairs. One of his colleagues said of him that he was not only a good physician but would have made his name running a departmental store or an oil company. His next move was masterly. At the London dinner of the Oxford Graduates Medical Club he arranged for Cairns to sit next to Sir Douglas Veale*, Registrar of the University. Veale was an ex-civil servant who had been Private Secretary to the first Minister of Health, Christopher Addison*, and to no fewer than five of his successors. He was well acquainted with the medical scene and had been privy to the Rockefeller discussions of 1927. Veale, although the servant of the University, had considerable influence in its affairs. Not for nothing was the registry known as the 'Hôtel de Veale', and there were even rumours of 'Veales within Veales.'

Both Cairns and Veale were men of great ability, drive and vision, and each was much impressed by the other. So here was a valuable ally on the University side. At Veale's suggestion, in March 1936 Cairns wrote a much fuller memorandum to Buzzard, who showed it to Lord Nuffield.

Later that year, as I described earlier, the annual meeting of the British Medical Association was held in Oxford, with Buzzard as President. I was one of the two secretaries and saw most of what went on. The meeting opened on Friday July 17th with a reception by the Vice-Chancellor. At this reception Cairns was introduced to Lord Nuffield, who invited him to come to his house at Huntercombe on the Sunday. On the Monday, according to custom, Buzzard gave a private dinner party for the top people and also kindly invited the two Secretaries. We wined and dined extremely well in All Souls College. As it was a pleasant summer evening, after dinner we strolled out on the lawns. Lord Nuffield, who had also dined well, suddenly said rather loudly: 'I am going to give a million and a quarter pounds to the medical school.' We all looked round and he was hustled into a corner out of earshot. The sum was later raised to two million pounds.

A document was drawn up about the Benefaction in general terms, but it was clear that there would be professors of medicine, surgery, and of obstetrics and gynaecology. Lord Nuffield expressed a wish for a professor of anaesthetics. Both Buzzard and Cairns thought that this was not an academic subject and resisted the proposal. The matter was settled very simply by his Lordship saying, in almost so many words, 'No chair of anaesthetics, no Benefaction.' Moreover he wished the first holder of the chair to be Robert Macintosh, of whose skill he had had first-hand experience. He was right. Sir Robert Macintosh, who thus became the first professor of this subject in the British Commonwealth, created a successful department which has made notable contributions to the theory and practice of anaesthesia.

By the end of the year electoral boards were announced. Hugh Cairns was appointed Professor of Surgery in January 1937, Robert Macintosh in Anaesthetics in February, Chassar Moir* in Obstetrics and Gynaecology in May. There were difficulties in the appointment to the Medicine chair. An eminent American was invited. He came to Oxford, took one look at what he regarded as the poor facilities and declined. Leslie Witts was elected in November.

The arrival of four ambitious and empire-building professors at the Radcliffe Infirmary, a small provincial hospital, can be compared only to four very large cuckoos in a very small nest. Some members of the medical staff and some lay members of the committee of management were violently opposed to their being allowed in the place at all. There were some spectacular rows and personal quarrels. One minor one occurred when a lay member of the University protested at the proposal to give each of the Nuffield Professors the degree of Doctor of Medicine. He was quite right. If an MA was good enough for Sir Charles Sherrington, President of the Royal Society and a Nobel Prize winner, it should have been good enough for new and untried Nuffield Professors. Things rumbled on for a time. Eventually, the chairman of the Infirmary Governors, Sir William Goodenough* (a tough banker), summoned the medical staff by three-line whip to a meeting on a Sunday morning, an unprecedented event. He said in effect: 'Look, you people. The Nuffield Benefaction is coming to the Infirmary, whether you like it or not, so you had better get used to it.'

In time the Professors did receive new wards and laboratories, and what seemed to us lavish facilities of every kind. A year before the advent of the Nuffield departments a new medical ward had been opened to my design and I was happily installed in it. The administration asked me if I would give it up to the Professor of Medicine. Of course I had to say yes, but this is just life. I was transferred to an old army hut, a relic of World War I. No one ever said thank you. It is possible to do good work in bad wards but it takes a little more effort. The outbreak of World War II in 1939 stopped controversy, and we were all busy doing other things.

42

The Nuffield professorships have been a success, but no world-shaking discoveries or Nobel Prizes have emerged. The last but one holder of the Medicine chair, Sir David Weatherall (now Regius Professor of Medicine) built a distinguished department of molecular medicine whose members include four Fellows of the Royal Society.

The war years (1939–1945)

I had been in the Territorial Royal Army Medical Corps since 1924, so in 1938, at the time of the Munich crisis, I was all packed up to go to a possible war. Despite Neville Chamberlain's comforting words 'Peace in our time', it was clear that there would be a war later on. In anticipation, the Emergency Medical Service was formed. The head of the Oxford area was Sir Robert McCarrison*, a retired major-general of the Indian Medical Service. In 1939 I was summoned to see him and was ordered to resign from the Territorials, chiefly on the grounds that someone 'had to look after the shop'. Naturally I felt bad about this, but did as I was told.

Like everybody else, our lives were altered by the war but much less so than had I remained in the Territorials. Our two maids and children's nanny left, but one general factotum girl remained. My wife remarked philosophically: 'At any rate I can now go into my own kitchen and not be scowled at.' Thirty years later she was heard to say: 'I would gladly go into my kitchen and be scowled at if I had a maid.'

Owing to the prospect of bombing there was a large exodus of women and children from London to Oxford. It was alleged that at Paddington Station there was a notice which read: 'All pregnant women must show their pink forms to the stationmaster.' We had a succession of evacuees, starting with three children from London's East End. They were natural thieves and within 48 hours had stolen and hidden all the family bicycle bells. They had nits, scratched their heads with their forks and spoke a language we could not understand. For example 'Airs ee up oo ink ee orer ou o?' meant 'Where's the cup you drink the water out of?' The twin boys liked to stand on the garden wall in full view of my consulting room and see who could pee the furthest. They were a trial to us, and were not happy sleeping in a large room in three separate beds instead of all being in one bed as at home. We found them more congenial quarters in Cowley. We had many other evacuees, some easy to accommodate, others less so.

I received a fierce letter from Robin Lawrence* complaining that there was no clinic in Oxford for his diabetic patients, so I started the diabetic clinic at the Radcliffe Infirmary. Charles Fletcher*, with my registrar and me, wrote a booklet of general guidance for our patients. Fortunately, just before it went to the printer, we noticed an unfortunate juxtaposition. The last line of a page read 'Pass a specimen of urine.' Immediately below was a footnote (that had overflowed from the previous page) which read 'To do this hold the tube in a flame.' We altered it.

In 1940, when invasion seemed possible, if not likely, Oxford University received an invitation from Yale and Swarthmore Universities to send children, and a few mothers to look after them, to the United States for safety. After numerous meetings and much anxious thought, we decided to accept and my wife did go with our three children. She was one of the few mothers allowed to travel because she had a child aged under five. I was in a spot because I was far too busy to run a home. Fortunately, my father and my sister Dorothy nobly left their home near Bournemouth and came to look after me till my wife returned six months later. Dorothy worked extremely hard, in effect running a free hotel for numerous family and friends from London who came down every weekend to escape the bombing. The children remained in the United States until the war was almost over.

Almost exactly 50 years after the evacuation to the United States there was a large party in Oxford attended by the evacuated children, their parents and a few of the hosts.

In 1942 the Churchill Hospital was built at Headington for the United States military forces, who occupied it until the end of the war. They were a friendly and hospitable lot. I sometimes attended their clinical meetings. After the war the hospital became part of the United Oxford Hospitals. In 1992 there was a delightful clinical meeting to celebrate its 50 years.

In 1942 I had the pleasant surprise of being elected a Fellow of Merton College, by virtue of being a Reader. This fellowship has been a source of constant interest and pleasure ever since.

In the winter of 1941–42 it snowed, thawed, froze, thawed and froze again with the result that every road was covered by a thin layer of invisible ice. In the ordinary way I would never have thought of taking my car out but I was asked to see a very ill patient in an outlying village, so off I went. Despite, as I thought, careful driving I skidded at the top of a hill. The car swung round through 90 degrees and slid down the hill sideways at increasing speed. At the bottom there was a loud bang as the car hit what looked like a telegraph pole and knocked it over. It turned out to be carrying the electricity supply to the village and surrounding area. The noise of the impact brought out the villagers, who took me in to render first aid to my cut scalp. I asked if I might use the telephone to explain that I had had an accident and could not come to the consultation.

My temporary host overheard me and said that he would take me. I protested but he insisted, so I arrived at a Palladian mansion in a small van labelled PLAIN AND FANCY PASTRY. FAMILIES WAITED ON DAILY, with no hat and lots of bloodstains. The most remarkable aspect of the incident was that just before the impact I suddenly saw the post about two feet away and approaching at great speed, I suppose at 20 mph. My computer tells me that to travel two feet at that speed takes about 1/15 of a second. During this very short time I had a long, leisurely think about the situation and can still remember it clearly. I thought: 'We are going to hit that post. It looks like being a nasty accident. I hope it won't be painful. I might even be killed. If I were, it would be very difficult for my wife and children. They would probably have to move to a smaller house. Even then they would be in financial trouble. It might be best if she married again for the sake of the children.' My car remained by the roadside for a fortnight, and the repairs included a new frame.

I was asked to examine a number of scientists who were engaged on some secret research connected with the war effort, and I too was pledged to strict secrecy. I had no idea what the research was about or what substances were involved. I can now reveal that it was to do with the atomic bomb. An interesting point was that by chatting to the scientists, pretending that I knew much more than I did and piecing together small pieces of evidence, by the fifth man I knew the formula of the substance they were using. If a number of people know a secret it seems bound to leak out.

I paid many visits to London, examining in the Conjoint, attending committees and occasionally for pleasure. The flying bombs could be heard approaching. When the noise stopped, there was a pause and then the explosion. The rockets were different. As they travelled faster than sound there was an explosion followed by a crescendo scream of the approach – alarming, but harmless. Pleasure was limited. My wife and I once stayed in London at the Cumberland Hotel, at Marble Arch, it is true for 11 shillings each for bed and breakfast, but all we each had for breakfast was two pickled walnuts. Food rationing lasted for 14 years.

When peace was declared in August 1945 the Government rightly gave high priority to bringing back to this country British soldiers from German prisoner-of-war camps. The Army showed how efficient it can be. Within 24 hours of being in a prisoner-of-war camp in Germany, each man had been issued with a pay book, ration book, railway warrant to his home and a form to fill in for the forthcoming parliamentary election. Most were able to go home, but those who looked ill were admitted to hospital to be checked, in particular for tuberculosis.

I had two wards full of these men. They were splendid. One man proudly showed me the clock from the camp commandant's office that he had pinched as a souvenir. Needless to say the hospital made great efforts to give them good meals, but once one of my ward sisters was almost in tears because she had found a man after a large dinner eating fish and chips that a friend had handed in through a window. Fortunately, none of the men had tuberculosis and they could go home after a few days.

During the war we were still living in Woodstock Road, a highly respectable residential area, most of the properties belonging to St John's College. Down the road from us an unsavoury gentleman opened a disorderly house for the benefit of American soldiers. I was invited to dine in St John's College and at dessert found myself sitting next to the President of the College. His opening conversational gambit was: 'Ah yes, Cooke, you live next door to one of our brothels in the Woodstock Road, don't you?'

When the war stopped the streets were thronged with cheering people, every woman and every child wearing garments which included red, white and blue.

CHAPTER EIGHT

The Oxford Clinical School

At the outbreak of war in September 1939 the London teaching hospitals were evacuated, among them St Bartholomew's to St Albans and St Thomas's to Hydestile, near Godalming. The prospect of bombing seemed likely to disrupt teaching. Attention to casualties would obviously take precedence over lecturing to students. Sir Farquhar Buzzard, who I suspect had been dreaming of a clinical school in Oxford for years, therefore invited the fifty Oxford students who had just completed their pre-clinical training and would normally have gone to London hospitals, to stay in Oxford, if they wished, for their hospital work. The majority accepted. So, at a stroke we had a clinical school but with no premises, no staff and no organization.

A few days later a meeting was held at my house with Buzzard, a few of the Radcliffe Infirmary staff and Sir Douglas Veale. Buzzard unfolded his plan and we all listened with polite interest. He then turned to me and said: 'You will run it. It will start next week.' Buzzard had a door cut in the wall separating the Radcliffe Infirmary from Somerville College and I was allotted three small rooms in the College, later used as my office, a common room, and a library. This area, within what was then an all women establishment, became known as the Isle of Man.

I seconded Audrey Rouse, my efficient and good-looking secretary, to the clinical school, bought a second-hand typewriter, had some stationery printed and allotted the students to their medical and surgical firms. So in ten days' time we did have a clinical school. To replace Audrey I employed her efficient and also good-looking sister, Valerie, as my private secretary. They were usefully interchangeable.

I was called the Clinical Subdean because there was already a Dean, who looked after the preclinical students. Later the name of the post was changed to Director of Clinical Studies.

The Infirmary staff was depleted by those away on war service, so Buzzard enlisted the help of other teachers. Sir Arthur Hurst's* New Lodge Clinic at Windsor had been commandeered for war purposes, so he moved to Oxford and was an enthusiastic teacher. We also had for

48

Director of clinical studies

surgery George Gask*, Leonard Findlay* for paediatrics and, for a time, Sir Max Page* for surgery. I remained in charge of the school for ten years. Despite the newness, informality and scratch nature of the school, its products more than held their own in the outer world.

In 1989 Professor John Ledingham, a distinguished Oxford physician, arranged a delightful dinner in New College for all ten of those who had directed the Clinical School over the previous fifty years. It was interesting to compare the original school, with one small office, a staff of one secretary, a second-hand typewriter and fifty students with the present-day school with extensive premises, a large staff, three computers, 300 students and an international reputation.

As the war in Europe drew to a close, the questions arose – What is to become of the Oxford Clinical School after the war? Was it a wartime

49

expedient or should it continue? These questions were propounded in an acute form when the University was asked to give evidence before the Interdepartmental Committee on Medical Schools (the Goodenough Committee). Evidence was taken from a number of teachers, students and other interested persons.

The majority report was to the effect that the present school should cease and be replaced by, or merge into, a special type of clinical school, small in numbers. It would aim to produce not general practitioners but only consultants, medical scientists and future professors. This, of course, was a crazy idea. How can anyone tell the future career of a young student aged 19? Enemies of the scheme used to refer to these specially selected students as the *Herrenvolk*. Anyhow, what is wrong with producing good general practitioners?

The clinical staff of the Radcliffe Infirmary were mostly in favour of continuation. Of the Nuffield Professors, some were for and some against. There were heated differences. I summarised the arguments for and against in an article in the *Oxford Magazine* of 17 May, 1945.

A CLINICAL SCHOOL AT OXFORD?

Clinical teaching at the Radcliffe Infirmary is no new thing. A month before the Infirmary was opened for the reception of patients in 1770, a plan was laid before the Governors for the admission of students in physic and surgery, but its execution was delayed until the first Litchfield Professor of Medicine was elected in 1780. By then clinical students were regularly admitted. Such records as are available show a maximum of eight in 1837, but the numbers diminished almost to vanishing point later in the century. In the twentieth century, at any rate between the two world wars, clinical teaching was limited to part-time instruction for six months of the year for the few students who stayed up [at Oxford] for the courses in Pathology, Bacteriology and Pharmacology. Also, before the 1939-45 war we took one or two students for some special reason – one was the widow of a science don who could not easily leave Oxford because of her young family.

On the outbreak of war in 1939 a complete clinical school was hurriedly established, actually at ten days' notice, and has continued to the present time. The sudden arrival of a teaching school threw a considerable strain on the staff of the Infirmary and the Nuffield Departments, which, apart from their new teaching duties, were burdened by the presence of many more patients than in peace time, while the numbers of the staff were depleted by the demands of the fighting services. Nevertheless, the school has surmounted these difficulties and produced young medical graduates who have at least held their own in the outside world with those from other teaching centres

It is plain that a Goodenough Committee type of school would present many problems and difficulties, technical, administrative and financial, and it is no secret that opinion in the Medical Faculty is still divided on the possibility of carrying out such a scheme, and indeed on the desirability of having it at all. Some non-medical members of the University may be interested to learn the salient pros and cons of the scheme, and all members of the University, medical or lay, should be aware of what is going on in a matter which concerns not only the welfare of the Medical School, but also that of the University as a whole. It is therefore proposed to give, without comment, some of the arguments put forward on both sides: first those in favour of the school, then those against it.

In Favour

• That undergraduate teaching was contemplated in the original scheme for the Nuffield Benefaction (Decree of December 1st, 1936: 'Provided always that nothing in this Decree shall be deemed to be inconsistent with the inclusion within the scope of the School of the instruction of students reading for the degree of BM').

• That the duties of Nuffield Professors were to include undergraduate instruction (Decree of December 1st, 1936: 'They shall give or hold such number of lectures or classes as the Committee shall determine.')

• That the presence of undergraduates is a stimulus to the work of a hospital – a stimulus to professors and their staffs, and a corrective to the rarefied atmosphere of postgraduate research.

That Oxford is well suited to provide a clinical school, with academic ideals and roots in University soil, where young men and women can be trained in the art and science of medicine without the material distractions common to so many of our great hospitals;

• That experience in undergraduate teaching is essential for the future preferment as professors of young assistants in the professorial departments.

• That Oxford is the ideal place for training future teachers, investigators and consultants.

• That as the school will be small it will not be a serious burden to the professorial units or to the staff of the Infirmary.

• That it will enable the heads of preclinical and clinical departments to keep in touch with promising recruits for their staffs.

Against

• That the Nuffield Medical Benefaction was primarily intended to foster research and that the Nuffield Professors and their staffs should be free to devote their whole time and energies to this work, unhampered by routine duties.

• That the presence of undergraduates is not essential to good hospital work or postgraduate studies and is in fact a time-consuming hindrance.

• That Oxford is not necessarily the best training ground for future teachers, investigators and consultants.

• That students who spend six or more years in Oxford will be out of touch with the realities of life as seen in hospitals in London and other large medical centres.

- That a small school requires approximately the same number of teachers and the same amount of teaching as a school of the usual size.
- That the Radcliffe Infirmary has not the buildings, equipment or staff for the type of school proposed.
- That it is quite impossible to select the right type of student for a future teacher, investigator or consultant at such an immature stage of development.
- That the school will die of inanition because the best students will continue to go to the London schools.

> *Who shall decide when doctors disagree*
> *and soundest casuists doubt, like you and me?*

The school did continue, but not in the *Herrenvolk* manner.

The National Health Service

In modern times, governmental interest in the health of the people dates from the 19th century. A convenient starting point is the cholera epidemic of 1831, which gave rise to the Central Board of Health. There followed a succession of numerous Public Health Acts and Factory Acts, the Poor Law Acts (which provided medical care only for paupers), the Old Age Pensions Act of 1908 (maximum payment 5s weekly, minimum 1s – and nothing if the annual income was over £30 10s) and Lloyd George's* National Insurance Act of 1911 (which provided medical care only for wage-earners, and not for their wives or children). Lloyd George regarded his Act as a first step and looked forward to a comprehensive medical service.

This was foreseen not only by the politicians but also by the medical profession. In 1918 Sir Bertrand Dawson (later Lord Dawson of Penn) in a lecture said that the treatment and prevention of disease should be available for every citizen irrespective of his position, by right and not by favour.

In 1919 the Ministry of Health was created. One of its first acts was to form a committee on this subject under the chairmanship of Lord Dawson. The period of gestation was long and the doctors were far ahead of the politicians. In 1929 the British Medical Association put forward its *Proposals for a General Medical Service for the Nation.* Governmental planning began in 1936. The first step was to survey the existing hospital facilities. In 1939 the war intervened, but did result in the formation of the Emergency Medical Service. This service worked well and provided useful information on planning the future peacetime service.

A White Paper which gave the general outline of the National Health Service was presented to Parliament in February 1944 and was debated in both Houses. In the Commons 33 members spoke, of whom four were medically qualified. One of the longest speeches was made by a member who had never even read the White Paper. Another member complained of the omission of any mention of osteopathy and of the cancer cure of a Dr Marshall who believed that this disease was caused by iron rust in the blood. Why was this not to be available to the public? Scandalous! The quality of the speeches was in inverse proportion to their length. In the Lords fifteen peers spoke, of whom, as in the Commons, four were medically qualified. Their speeches were shorter and much more to the point than those in the Commons. The National Health Service Bill became law in November 1946, and the Act came into operation in July 1948.

I regard the National Health Service as the greatest piece of social engineering ever carried out in this country. My admiration for the concept of the service derives from the fact that until it came into operation there were whole counties in the United Kingdom without a single consulting physician, surgeon, or obstetrician. Other specialties such as dermatology, ENT surgery, orthopaedics, paediatrics and pathology were also lacking. Now there are medical facilities of a good standard in every part of the country. Certainly, local general practitioners did a great deal of good work in hospitals, but the increasing complexity and technology of medicine require more than that now. The service has relieved the poor from medical fees, which could be financially crippling or high enough to prevent people from seeking much-needed advice for themselves and their children.

The official estimate of the annual cost of the service by Lord Beveridge*, an eminent economist, was £240 million, which proved to be wildly wrong and well illustrates the two basic laws of economics:

1. Your prediction will be wrong,
2. It will cost more than you ever thought possible.

In the first year the service cost twice as much as the estimate, and, of course, has risen annually since. Lord Beveridge also held the naïve belief that as the service improved the health of the nation, so the cost would go down. The cost has now risen to £36 billion, that is 150 times as much as the first estimate. Even allowing for 45 years of inflation, that is an enormous increase.

It is difficult to comprehend these vast numbers. If you were to count at the rate of two a second for 24 hours a day and seven days a week, it would take nearly six days to count a million, over 15 years to count a billion and over 500 years to count the cost of the National Health Service. Unfortunately, there is practically no limit to what can be spent on a health service. If every doctor in the service had every facility that he thought necessary for first-class work, the cost would be doubled overnight.

In my own case, I worked in the Oxford hospitals for 34 years, half of this time in the NHS. I had to make bricks without straw. I needed, and would have done better work with, another houseman or registrar, another secretary, a small laboratory and a research assistant. I just had to do without.

In 1948 we all had to decide whether or not to join the National Health Service. It was a difficult decision, as we had no idea what the service was going to be like. To help us, the Regional Hospital Board had kindly arranged for a special official to be available to discuss any problems. He turned out to be a doctor who had returned from a post in India only two days before and knew even less about it than we did. At one time there was a rumour, which must have been false, that if we did not join we would cease to be on the staff of the Radcliffe Infirmary. In the event we all did join. It made very little difference to our work and there was something to be said for a regular stipend and an index-linked pension.

In addition to the normal stipend, a system of merit awards was introduced, A, B and C and, later, A+. These were often criticized by laymen because they were secret but it would never do to make them public. Every patient would wish to be treated only by the holder of an A+ award which would be impracticable and unfair to the large numbers of able doctors who do not hold such an award. Also, the award might have been given for scientific research and not for clinical ability. I started with a B award, later received an A and ended with an A+.

Like the majority of doctors I spent a good deal more time on the service than I was paid for. Much as I admire the NHS and have enjoyed working in it, I sometimes used to pine for complete independence and the absence of bureaucracy. When I first went to the Radcliffe Infirmary in 1933 there was an administrator, Arthur Sanctuary (who in November 1991 reached the age of 100), with one clerk. The place ran like clockwork. There are now numerous administrators, a large clerical staff and an air of bureaucracy. The place certainly does not run so smoothly.

Index-linked pensions are not as protective as they appear at first sight. In the good old days, if I bought a new motor car it cost between a tenth and a fifth of my annual income – the same car today would cost about half my income.

One of the major troubles of the NHS is the increasing technology of medicine. When I started in medicine, my chief pieces of apparatus were a five-shilling stethoscope and a £2 sphygmomanometer. Now apparatus for ultrasound and nuclear magnetic resonance costs something in six figures. A modern X-ray department costs about £500,000. To make matters worse, if the hospital in town A acquires such a piece of apparatus, the hospital in town B, 30 miles away, claims that it must have one too or its patients will die from not being properly investigated and treated.

I here make a plea for cottage hospitals. National Health Service administrators do not like them and seek to have them closed. A country patient with an illness not requiring modern technology is much happier in a small friendly hospital near home, family and friends, and is not taking up an expensive bed in a teaching hospital. I have always admired the devoted women who are the matrons of cottage hospitals, often combining that office with doing the cooking and stoking the boiler.

I felt it my duty to read the recent White Paper on the future of the service. I regard myself as fairly educated and experienced but I just could not understand it – a thick prose style and bureaucratic jargon. However, despite the activities of politicians and bureaucrats, I think and hope that the National Health Service will continue to give valuable and irreplaceable service. From my personal point of view, one of the most satisfactory things about the service is that so far (1994) I have drawn my pension for eleven years longer than I worked to earn it.

I conclude with a strange fact. In 1992 there were several cases of unqualified men working in hospitals as consultants, either with forged evidence of qualification or no evidence at all. In my years of practising medicine I have never once been asked to produce any evidence of my qualification.

Quasi-medical activities

As seniority approaches, physicians are usually asked to undertake all kinds of quasi-medical activities, some of which are interesting and some even useful. I call them 'quasi-medical' because they take the physician away from the patient's bedside. They include committees, examining, giving lectures, attending conferences at home and abroad, serving in societies and the Royal Colleges, writing, editing journals, supporting student sports and similar organisations, and medical politics. Sometimes one accepts the invitation with pleasure and sometimes from a sense of duty. I seem to have had my share of these activities.

Committees

I regard myself as the worst committee man in the United Kingdom. I dislike and distrust committees as a method of getting things done. If I don't fall asleep from sheer boredom, I speak passionately on some topic which is not on the agenda or has already been decided at the last meeting. I have, of course, been compelled to sit on many committees.

Despite what I have just said, I have to confess that there was one committee I did enjoy. When the great John Hunter* died in 1793 his collection of anatomical, surgical and zoological specimens was bought by the nation and put in the care of the Royal College of Surgeons. To manage it, the Hunterian Trustees were created. They include the Lord Chancellor, the First Lord of the Treasury (who is the Prime Minister), the Chancellor of the Exchequer, the Speaker of the House of Commons, the President of the Royal Society and a few more ordinary people, of whom for a time I was one by virtue of being a Censor of the Royal College of Physicians.

The Trustees meet only at long intervals, so often the first item on the agenda is to stand in silence for the members who have died since the last meeting. Next are read apologies for absence from the Lord Chancellor, the Prime Minister, the Chancellor of the Exchequer, the Speaker of the

House of Commons, and the President of the Royal Society, all of whom express their great regret at being unable to attend on this particular occasion. It is probable that none has ever attended during the 200 years of the committee's existence. Next comes tea with unusually good smoked salmon sandwiches. Finally we transact a small amount of entirely non-controversial business. The perfect committee.

Examinations

I have always enjoyed examining. Apart from the obvious advantage of being on the right side of the table, one meets pleasant candidates and fellow examiners, has a chance to see other universities, medical schools and hospitals, has one's ignorance revealed and can learn.

I have examined in London (Conjoint and Membership), Oxford, Cambridge, Manchester and Dublin (Irish Conjoint). I have had to refuse London University and an attractive invitation in continental Europe from pressure of other work. Setting the questions has been no trouble, except for the Membership of the Royal College of Physicians of London in 'the good old days', when one of the Censors had to provide pieces of French, German, Latin and Greek for translation and – what is much worse – the answers.

The translations were discontinued, partly because fewer and fewer candidates attempted them and partly because the Censors came to realize, first, that they carried too large a proportion of the marks, and second, that a candidate who happened to come from Central Europe had a special advantage with the French and German. Correcting the scripts, especially if they are illegible or illiterate or both, is not very enjoyable. The clinicals, where one meets the examiners, the candidates and the patients, are by far the best part.

In the Conjoint clinical the patients have to come to the examination hall, so must be mobile and not acutely ill. They therefore have chronic diseases; most have attended on many occasions and most know all about their diagnosis. They often take a sporting interest in the event. I have been asked by a patient: 'Did my gentleman do all right?' They even administer a sort of rough justice. If a candidate is polite, gentle and has clean hands they help him. If he is rough or rude, they lead him astray. During the war, after a fierce air raid the night before, one of the examiners and two candidates did not turn up but every patient did. Good Londoners, they knew how important they were and were not going to miss 2s 6d and a free lunch.

Examiners tend to be entertained, especially in Cambridge where I sometimes felt a little like a premature baby because I was nourished every two hours. In contrast, at University College Hospital my host, who had better be nameless, after lunch said: 'You pay at the desk.'

The most remarkable examination in which I have taken part was the Irish Conjoint. No one knew what time it started, what ward it was in and sometimes even in which hospital, but in some miraculous way they got by. I discovered that the candidates, who often knew more about the venue than the examiners, used to ring up the house physicians and ask what patients they were going to be shown. As I was the only external examiner and also a member of the General Medical Council, I ventured to protest, but it had very little effect. On one occasion, of 97 candidates only two were of United Kingdom origin. The others came from all over the world. The Europeans were mostly Norwegians, who were there because their government found it cheaper to send them to Dublin than to build a new medical school. To do this requires institutes of chemistry, physics, botany, zoology, anatomy, physiology, biochemistry, pathology and pharmacology, all very costly, not to mention a large new hospital. Eire is of course a republic but we were taken to the *Royal* College of Physicians, the *Royal* College of Surgeons and dined at the *Royal* Irish Yacht Club. The slight eccentricities of the Irish Conjoint were as nothing to those of the Dublin Apothecaries' Hall. This institution was founded in the 18th century. It was originally concerned with pharmacy, but somehow became able to give a registrable qualification, Licentiate of the Apothecaries' Hall of Dublin. The General Medical Council always disapproved of it and tried unsuccessfully on several occasions to have it abolished. This can be done only by the Privy Council. Eventually it was discovered that at one examination, as none of the candidates could speak English, the whole proceedings were conducted in dumb show. Later revelations that the questions, and even the answers, were being sold to candidates, led the Privy Council to remove the Hall's power to give a registrable qualification.

Some of my happiest examination recollections derive from Donald Hunter*, a physician to the London Hospital and a man of immense energy with a fine disregard for the ordinary conventions. He had a sometimes fierce manner, but was a generous marker. On one occasion a candidate gave an answer of which Donald strongly disapproved. He shouted at the candidate: 'What's your medical school?' The candidate told him.

'Who's your professor?' The candidate named him.

'Did he teach you that?'

'Yes.'

'Well, when you get home, shoot him.'

Donald was an expert on industrial medicine and at *vivas* produced various exhibits, such as lumps of metal, asbestos, tar, and bricks. During the war, one morning before he arrived, we removed his exhibits and replaced them by items from a neighbouring bomb dump – a bicycle wheel, a broken milk bottle and an old shoe. He rushed in and put the remains of the milk bottle in front of a startled candidate, who said: 'It looks like part of a milk bottle.'

'Yes, tell me some diseases transmitted by milk.'

On another occasion Donald received an answer that he did not like in a *viva*. Being a born teacher he gave the candidate a lecture. When the bell sounded he asked me how many marks the candidate should have. I replied: 'He has only said three words, but you were very good and deserve about 70.' On another occasion, I am told, Donald had a crocodile skin dispatch case. He asked a candidate what would be the dangers for a man making such a case. The candidate, older and more mature than most, said: 'I have very little knowledge of the dangers of working in the plastics industry.'

Lectures

People are asked to give lectures for various reasons. Someone has to give the routine lectures to the students. A friend asks you as a compliment. Someone thinks you have certain special knowledge which should be revealed to the world. The Royal Colleges have numerous endowed lectures that must be given by somebody. Most of us enjoy being asked to lecture because it is a mark of respect and provides publicity. On the other hand, very few, if any, doctors have been taught how to lecture. It may be a natural gift but usually has to be learnt.

Lecturing is good training for a physician. He has to think about the subject seriously, put his thoughts in order and present them in a logical and digestible form. I usually lecture from a few headings on a postcard, but when I was asked to give the Lumleian* Lectures at the Royal College of Physicians of London I thought that this was a serious matter, especially as William Harvey had earlier featured in the same series. I decided to read the two lectures and this is a difficult art, so I took lessons from an elocution teacher. I learnt that you must not have long sentences like Lord Macaulay* but short sentences like Winston Churchill*. I ended by having each sentence marked where the chief stress was, and in some the secondary stress as well.

When Lord Moran gave the Harveian Oration at the Royal College of Physicans he spoke without any script and two seconds after he had finished, the clock struck the hour. He must have learnt it like the part in a play. I have known some other remarkable lecturers. Sir William MacArthur*, a former Director-General of the Army Medical Services, gave detailed lectures on tropical medicine and public health without a note and without a word out of place. Donald Hunter once lectured to the Oxford students on industrial medicine. After more than an hour and about a hundred slides, they wanted more. Lord Brain*, the distinguished neurologist, used to say that if during your lecture the audience looked at their watches there was no need to worry, but if they started shaking them to see if they were going it was nearing the time to stop. Medical lectures have sometimes been unfairly described as 'casting false pearls before real swine.'

Conferences

Of conferences there is no end, and they show great variety. The typical unsatisfactory conference is in an inconvenient place at the wrong time of the year. The two papers that you specially wish to hear are given simultaneously in two different buildings. A few of the papers are good, but many merely illustrate the adage 'Sweet are the uses of advertisement.' On the other hand, the venue may be in a delightful place and the company good. I recollect particularly enjoyable occasions in Stockholm, New York, Oslo and Cairo.

I have usually learnt more about medicine from talking to colleagues in the bar than from the formal presentations. The conference that I have most often attended is that of the Association of Physicians of Great Britain and Ireland, more than 50 times. The association meets annually, every fifth year in London and in the other years in turn in the universities of the United Kingdom and Ireland.

My first introduction to the Association was in 1930 when I read a paper at the meeting in London. It was an unnerving experience because I did not then know Sir Arthur Hurst. He was deaf, always sat in the front row as near as possible to the speaker, and wore a cumbersome hearing aid. If he did not find a paper interesting he removed the earpiece, laid it on the desk before him and usually forgot to switch it off, so it made loud screeching noises. I was elected to the Association in 1936.

The Association's journal, *The Quarterly Journal of Medicine,* was founded in 1907 by Sir William Osler in a typically informal way. He walked into the offices of the Oxford University Press with a junior colleague, Dr A. G. Gibson*, and said to the Secretary of the Press: 'We are going to have a journal. He will look after it', and to Gibson: 'If you want anything, ask him.' Gibson was Secretary to the editors and later an editor for 30 years until I took over from him as Secretary to the editors in 1937. I had had no experience whatever in editorial work. In the first number of the journal to come out under my direction I discovered a misprint that had been overlooked by the OUP reader – an e instead of an i. Very pleased with myself, I crossed out the e and put an i in the margin. To make sure that the printer did not overlook this important correction I underlined the i. Printers take underlining to indicate italics; as a result there is a single italic i in a whole page of roman type, the Cooke memorial *i*.

On one occasion the editors accepted a paper which I thought was bad, so much so that I remarked to my secretary that the proper place for it was the wastepaper basket. A few days later when I asked her to take the manuscript to the printer she could not find it. Diligent search was made, with no success. We then realized that we had recently had a drive to get rid of waste paper. We rushed to the dustbins but they had been emptied. I rang the city engineer to find the whereabouts of our corporation rubbish vehicle. My wife, my secretary and I rushed off to the dump to find a large lorry full of paper being tipped up to be emptied. We shouted 'Stop, stop!' and explained our problem. We waded into the mountain of paper. The dustmen took a sporting interest in the search and kept offering us any piece of paper that they could not understand. Just as we were about to give up in despair I found one page of the references and eventually we retrieved the whole manuscript. We were also lucky that owing to the war the paper was kept separate from the other rubbish for recycling. Otherwise we would have been searching among cinders, potato peelings, fish bones, porridge, and other unpleasant matter. I was so relieved that I pressed £1 notes on everybody in sight.

I made a vow never to throw anything away again, but Fate intervened. A year later I discarded my little book that contained the year's appointments and engagements. Again the dustbins had been emptied. My secretary, splendid girl, by then fully trained, dashed off to the dump to find that the paper had all been baled. Using her charm she managed to persuade the workmen to undo one of the bales. By a freak of good fortune it contained my book. I made a new vow never again to throw anything away.

I later became an editor of the *Quarterly Journal* and eventually chairman of the editorial board. When I retired in 1966 my knowledge of the shortcomings of authors was extensive. One author, to support his (or was it her?) views, quoted an extract from a book. It seemed remarkably inappropriate for its purpose so I went to the library, looked it up and found that the passage had been correctly copied except for omission of the word 'not'. Another author who had contributed a paper ten years before asked whether, if the type was still standing, he could have some more offprints. I have to confess that when *I* write an article the editor usually finds some error of fact or presentation.

Royal College of Physicians

At the Royal College of Physicians of London I have served as an examiner for the Conjoint and the Membership, a Councillor, Third Censor, Second Censor and Senior Censor. I gave the Lumleian Lecture on *Osteoporosis* in 1955, the Langdon-Brown Lecture on *The College and Europe* in 1968 and a Christmas Lecture on *Leonardo da Vinci* in 1976. It runs in the family – my son John gave a Christmas Lecture in the following year on *Spiders*. Osteoporosis, although extremely common, did not receive much notice then. I consulted the latest editions of ten leading textbooks of medicine. One gave the subject forty lines, one eight lines, one six lines and two four lines. The other five did not mention it at all. Postmenopausal osteoporosis, now in the news, was mentioned by only two of the ten books.

It seems that if you write about a disease you tend to contract it. I now have osteoporosis and have gone down over six inches in height. This has had a deplorable effect on my wardrobe. I now wear long teddy boy type jackets, and I am not in a position to renew my wardrobe every few years.

When I was an officer of the Royal College of Physicians Sir Isaac Wolfson* gave the college a generous donation, so we entertained him and his family to dinner. We started with smoked salmon and champagne, which seemed promising, but it turned out that the Wolfsons were strict Jews so the main course was scrambled eggs. It was a terrible let-down.

The Royal College of Physicians has greatly changed in the sixty years that I have known it. In the past it has been extremely conservative and remote from real life. An interesting illustration occurred during the cholera epidemic of 1892. The Local Government Board asked the College for hygienic advice to be given to the public. A committee produced some sensible suggestions on cleanliness, boiling water and milk, and sanitation, but also advised the poor of London to eat three or four ample meals a day and to avoid certain sparkling wines.

Thirty years ago when the President, Treasurer, and Registrar were unmarried men and the College Secretary a spinster, in the words of Henry Miller* the College was run by 'three elderly bachelors called Miss Cook'. Today the College is extremely active, with numerous conferences and a nationwide – indeed a worldwide – influence. The Membership examination takes place in numerous foreign countries because it is regarded as a high-class higher qualification and cannot be obtained by bribing the examiners.

The College has shown its modernity and common sense by electing, after only 471 years, its first woman President, Dame Margaret Turner-Warwick, who proved to be an excellent choice. The College has been more progressive than the City of London, which took 800 years to elect its first woman Lord Mayor. On the other hand, after nearly 500 years, in 1992 the College decided to give up sending out the summons to meetings in Latin, in my view a deplorable manifestation of modernity and what we sometimes laughingly refer to as progress.

Royal Society of Medicine

The Royal Society of Medicine was formed in 1807 by the amalgamation of most of the London medical societies. They tended to be in financial difficulties and some were saved from extinction by the amalgamation. The Harveian and Hunterian Societies remained independent. I joined the Royal Society of Medicine in 1924, chiefly to use the excellent library. From an interest in the history of medicine I was elected a Vice-President of that section, which is usually a prelude to being President. As I was extremely busy at the time I did not attend a single meeting that year, so quite rightly my name was removed.

In 1961 I was elected President of the section of medicine, a most pleasant two-year task. All the work was done by the two secretaries. All I had to do was to discuss the programme, give the speakers dinner and try to look intelligent. In those days it was a vigorous and successful section. There was one occasion when the Barnes Hall was packed. From the dais I had a clear view of the audience (of about 200) and noticed that in the two hours of the meeting only two cigarettes were smoked. The doctors had got the message. Later on the ravages of specialization caused the section to wither away, and it was broken up into several more specialized sections.

In 1972, forty-eight years after joining it, I was elected an Honorary Fellow of the Society. There are 100 of them, 70 in this country and 30 in the rest of the world. In June 1986, when the Queen, with the Duke of Edinburgh, opened the new building, the Honorary Fellows were put in a comfortable lounge with armchairs and refreshments, while the generality of Fellows had to stand in the main building. It all looked promising, but coming up to London in the bus I suddenly realized that I had left my false teeth behind. They are not complete, but it did leave some awkward gaps. I had short conversations with the Queen and the Duke of Edinburgh, trying not to open my mouth. The President introduced me to the Queen by saying: 'Dr Cooke was a pupil of Sir William Osler.' The Queen smiled sweetly but I am sure that she had never heard of the Regius Professor of Medicine at Oxford in 1919. I had brought with me a lady friend and before the ceremony had taken her out to lunch. She ate a substantial meal. All I managed was soup, avocado and asparagus. On the way home I decided to write an *Edentulous Cookbook* for those in similar trouble.

General Medical Council

In 1963 I was appointed to represent Oxford University on the General Medical Council, then under the presidency of Lord Cohen of Birkenhead*. He was a remarkable man and had a phenomenal memory. In a long and complicated case he might say to a witness: 'But on Tuesday you said so and so.' The shorthand transcript would be consulted and showed that Cohen was word for word correct. The Council is such a large body that it can deal only with predigested business, so most of the work is done by committees. I served on several, of which the most interesting was the Disciplinary Committee. The offences of doctors run on well-known lines, mostly related to alcohol, drugs or sex, but we did make history by, for the first time in over 100 years, crossing off a woman doctor for having seduced a male patient.

Since my day the Council has been humanized. The President, Registrar and legal assessor used to sit on a raised dais while the accused was confined to a 'dock.' Now the President sits at ground level and the accused sits in a chair. Another improvement is that it is now realized that not all who commit offences against the Council's rules are criminals but may be the victims of old age or ill health, and such cases are now dealt with by different machinery. The Council has also been improved by the addition of more lay members. I think its humanization should be carried still further: at present, of whatever offence a doctor is accused, his name is given, and the media at once seize on the spicy details. If the accused is acquitted he has been publicly pilloried and a lot of the mud is bound to stick. It would be fairer if the name were revealed only on conviction.

Sometimes accused doctors have offered the defence that they did not know that what they had done was wrong, and have asked to be told what they may and may not do. In English law 'ignorance of the law is no excuse.' This obviously must be so or it would be the universal defence, but it is flattering that we are all supposed to know the whole of this very large and complicated subject. Of course, it should not be necessary to tell any doctor that he must not commit such acts as murder, forgery, robbery with violence, theft, rape, arson or fraud. With regard to less serious offences, over a hundred years ago a doctor was crossed off the register for 'exhibiting waxworks of an indecent nature.' I still think that it would be unnecessary and absurd to say to a newly qualified young doctor: 'Now, whatever you do, you must not exhibit waxworks of an indecent nature.'

Medical writing

If new medical knowledge is to be disseminated it must be done by writing as well as by word of mouth. This has led to a vast, unconsidered and sometimes chaotic medical literature, much of which is of little or no value. If a really conscientious doctor took all the medical journals in the world he would require another mile of shelf space in his library every 18 months. The adage 'publish or perish' has much to answer for. The result is that we are so swamped with information that important papers can be overlooked.

The botanist and monk Gregor Mendel*, although a Czech, wrote in German. His paper, which practically founded the study of heredity, was ignored for 34 years, no doubt because it was buried in a mass of unimportant papers. Selection committees are apt to notice how many publications a candidate has produced but seldom bother to read them. The citation index, an American invention, is not as reliable as hoped because, I suspect, a lot of cross-citation goes on by arrangement.

Medical politics

I have taken very little part in medical politics. I regard it as somebody else's job, like driving railway trains or cleaning drains. I have belonged to the British Medical Association since 1924 and been the secretary of the Oxford branch, have read the *Journal*, have given a few lectures, attended a few lectures and have (with a slight sense of guilt) eaten a few dinners provided by drug companies. That is the extent of my involvement in medical politics.

Physical exercise

My involvement in student athletics has been similarly tenuous. I was once vice-president of the St Thomas's Hospital Hockey Club. I have never played that game or had any intention of doing so. In Rugby football you do at least fight with bare hands, in hockey you are armed with a large wooden club. Besides, there are the dangers of march fracture and march haemoglobinuria, troubles caused by taking violent exercise. I have always found it safer to lie down than take exercise. I used to belong to the Stewards' Enclosure at Henley Royal Regatta solely for the pleasure of watching other people grossly overexerting themselves.

The study of architecture is a good poor man's hobby. Nobody can stop you looking at a building and you can often talk your way inside.

I have to confess that the last paragraph is a slight exaggeration. I have been guilty of exercise. For many years I was a keen student of Judo and Kendo, that is, Japanese wrestling and sword fighting. Judo, which means 'the way of gentleness', is different from Jujitsu, which means 'the art of gentleness.' The difference is that Judo has higher moral principles, such as never attacking anybody but acting only in self defence. Kendo is practised only with bamboo swords, and one is appropriately protected by armour.

It is important for doctors to have two recreations, preferably an outdoor one for summer and an indoor one for winter. Many years ago, in a bout of unwarranted enthusiasm, I took to rising early in the morning to run in the University Parks. On one occasion the red Sun was rising just over my left shoulder and I was horrified to see in front a blood-red rainbow. A portent of this kind could not be ignored and I never ran again. I thought the newspapers would be full of this remarkable phenomenon but there were no other lunatics up early enough to see it.

Present hobbies

Now, apart from reading (fact, not fiction) my interests are chiefly in medicine, the study of people, travel and the study of architecture. The last is a good poor man's hobby. No one can stop you looking at a building and you can often talk your way inside. One of the few advantages of old age is that you forget about the books that you have read and can have all the pleasure of rediscovering them. In the last sentence I used the words 'old age.' I should have said 'incipient maturity.' Another name for an old person is a 'recycled teenager'.

About the medical profession

At the time of writing there are about 140,000 names on the Medical Register, which is just over 50 per cent of all those ever registered since the Medical Act of 1858. The great majority are honest, hard-working men and women with the highest professional standards, but among 150,000 people there are bound to be a few who lapse below accepted standards. If one considers how easy it is to cheat and defraud patients, it is remarkable how well the profession behaves. For example, suppose a doctor says to a patient with a condition likely to make a spontaneous recovery that it is a serious condition, possibly fatal, but that there is a remedy which unfortunately can be obtained only from a laboratory in Switzerland, and is very expensive. The patient, in fear of his life, is likely to ask for this remedy, even if it does cost £100 for each injection. The doctor gives six injections of normal saline, and the patient recovers. Both parties are delighted.

Apart from serious fraud like this, the profession does have some minor failings. One is the use of the deplorable phrase 'we are on the verge of a breakthrough.' What this really means is 'we have not yet discovered anything that matters, but with luck something may turn up.' The first statement is eagerly taken up by the media; the speaker receives undeserved publicity and even more undeserved credit, while the hopes of patients are falsely raised. What constitutes a breakthrough? Surely events such as the introduction of anaesthetics, antisepsis, asepsis, the discovery of insulin, sulphonamides, penicillin, antimalarials and more recently keyhole surgery.

A minor fault, mostly confined to the newly-qualified, is fear of being caught out. This makes them say things like 'query tip of spleen *just* palpable.' This covers them whether the spleen is enlarged or not. They must be taught not to haver like this but to say outright whether they can or cannot feel the spleen.

Another fault is for an ambitious doctor to announce in the lay press that some medical condition is being badly treated in hospitals all over the country. The obvious inference is that he knows more about the subject than anybody else or that he is cleverer than all the other doctors. A feature of this kind of conduct is that it spreads alarm and despondency among the public.

Some ambitious doctors go in for empire building. They have a compulsion to 'build up a department' that is larger than anybody else's, but this is often achieved at the expense of their colleagues. There is some truth in the vulgar phrase 'he who shouts loudest gets most.'

A common medical bad habit is to refer to the size of tumours or lesions not in centimetres or inches but by comparison with common objects such as grapes, chestnuts, oranges, melons, eggs or golf balls, and on one memorable instance with a *large* golf ball! In 1960 we proposed having a small exhibition of these absurdities at a medical conference in Oxford and began to collect material. Much of this was easy, but I was anxious to obtain a Kansas sales tax ticket to which a lesion had been compared in an American book. I therefore wrote to a friend in the United States, Joe Garland, editor of *The New England Journal of Medicine*, and asked for his help. He kindly enquired of a colleague in Kansas who reported that when the sales tax tickets were introduced nobody used them because it was less trouble to pay the tax in coin, so the Kansas sales tax ticket no longer exists and is unobtainable. Dr Garland also sent me an example from an intern who, by percussion, located a pulmonary lesion which he described as the size of a hickory nut – with the shell on. It is high time that this nonsense was stopped.

An almost universal failing is the use, and misuse, of abbreviations and acronyms. When speaking on this subject I have used three lantern slides, all examples taken from Oxford hospitals. The first (for beginners) showed TPR (temperature, pulse and respiration), R & L (right and left), PA (pernicious anaemia), PMA (progressive muscular atrophy), BP (blood pressure). But there was another BP (bedpan). If you say to a nurse 'BP four hourly', what is she to do? Then there was CCF (congestive cardiac failure) and CSF (cerebrospinal fluid).

The second slide (for more advanced students) showed MBC (maximum breathing capacity), GFR (glomerular filtration rate), ADH (antidiuretic hormone), MCHC (mean corpuscular haemoglobin concentration), FTM (fractional test meal), WTM (will take message). The nurses too have become infected. They use HPU (has passed urine), NPU (has not passed urine), NCT (not come through) which means no blood showing on the dressing of a wound or operation, and DNSVI (does not seem very ill). Then, of course, there were DNA (deoxyribonucleic acid), and also DNA (did not attend) and LSCS (lower segment caesarean section).

The third slide (for those seeking honours) included EUAPNS (examination under anaesthesia of the post nasal space), TRINB (to return if need be), TPWOBA (trial puncture and wash out of both antra). I must explain the background of the next example. If a patient with defective vision is asked to look through a pinhole and the vision is improved, glasses may help. If the vision is not improved, it means that the defective vision is not due to an error of refraction, but to something else, such as retinopathy. This test is widely used in the diabetic clinic. The abbreviation is NICPH (not improved *cum* pinhole). Note the Latin word *cum*, just to show that we are still a learned profession.

The prize exhibit, from the Oxford Eye Hospital, was LAVIIULLL-RBSR. As you will readily guess, it means 'local anaesthesia of the 7th nerve, upper lid, lower lid and retrobulbar space on the right side.'

Matters are made worse by the fact that different hospitals and different doctors have their own peculiar abbreviations. Some of the examples I have given may seem amusing, but picture the scene at three o'clock in the morning with a seriously ill patient when a vital decision has to be made and nobody can understand the notes.

A pernicious form of abbreviation is the unnecessary acronym. A speaker at the Association of Physicians once showed a slide entitled 'chronic bronchitis.' To make quite sure that the audience would know exactly what he was talking about, the title was followed by (CB).

Speakers at such meetings often lecture on highly specialized subjects from which they acquire a jargon which eventually becomes their language, so that those not in their field have no idea what they are talking about. At a recent meeting of the Association of Physicians I took a counter with me and from the first day's papers collected 56 acronyms, many of which I had never heard of. 'Ah,' you will say, 'you are old and hopelessly out of date.' I have a feeling that I am not the only one. *The Oxford Companion to Medicine*, a book for the intelligent layman, has an appendix showing 1,700 medical acronyms. I wonder how many doctors know them all. Is your acronym really necessary?

Medical schools form a large, expensive and complex part of any university. Indeed the story is told of a vice-chancellor whose many failings finally landed him in hell. The Devil said: 'Your grave offences demand severe punishment, so I am appointing you as head of a new university.' The vice-chancellor, much relieved, said: 'That is not too bad. I have done this sort of job before.' 'Yes,' said the Devil, 'but this university has two medical schools.'

Having attended fifty-three meetings of the Association of Physicians and listened to countless other speakers, I have learned something about the presentation of papers. Obviously the speaker must know his subject thoroughly and would be wise to know something of the surrounding area, about which he may well be asked questions in the discussion.

There is a temptation to start the paper with an unusual and arresting sentence which will arouse the interest of the audience. This is a mistake, because the audience seldom listens to the opening sentence. Everybody finishes the conversation that he or she is having with their neighbour. They then rustle their papers and look to see what the next communication is about. The first sentence should be of no importance. When the audience is really listening you can bring in your clever and arresting sentence. The speaker should adjust the position of the microphone to match his height: it should be level with his mouth. He should not roam about the platform while he is speaking because the moment he departs from the microphone he will become inaudible to many of the audience

Another bee in my bonnet concerns lantern slides. The speaker, who of course knows the slide intimately, seldom seems to realize that the audience has never seen it before, and unless he tells them what it is about they will never know. If it is a graph he should explain the ordinates and abscissae, and if necessary the time scale. Slides should be legible; do not show slides that look like railway timetables; those based on typescript are seldom legible behind the front two rows; lines should be thick; there is often too much material on one slide and no time for the audience to take it all in. On a memorable occasion at the Association of Physicians an eminent professor of medicine showed a slide consisting entirely of figures, about twenty columns of twenty figures. It looked like a log table. I happened to time it – it was on the screen for nine seconds. A modern failing is to have slides made in various fancy colours. Black on white or white on black are more legible. Finally, a good slide shows one thing and shows it clearly.

Another failing is to use grander words than your rivals. A good example is 'parameter', which my dictionary says means:

1. **In mathematics.** In conic sections, the third proportional to any given diameter and its conjugate (or, in the parabola to any abscissa on a given diameter and the corresponding ordinate); this is the parameter of the given diameter. Specially the parameter of the transverse axis i.e. the latus rectum or focal chord perpendicular to the axis.

2. **Generally.** A quantity which is constant (as distinct from the ordinary variables) in a particular case considered, but which varies in different cases, especially a constant occurring in the equation of a curve or surface, by the variation of which the equation is made to represent a family of such curves or surfaces.

3. **In astronomy.** The data necessary to determine the orbit of a heavenly body.

4. **In crystallography.** Each of the intercepts made upon the axes in a crystal by the plane which is chosen for a face of the unit or primary pyramid.

It is certain that very few of the medical men and women who use the word 'parameter' have the faintest idea of its meanings. It is often all too plain that the word is used merely to be 'with it' and to cloak the most ordinary data with a spurious air of scientific learning. It could be replaced by some ordinary words such as 'limiting factor', 'measurement', 'aspect', or 'feature'.

A sad fact is that the compilers of dictionaries do not indicate what is the correct use of a word. They give, without comment, only the current usage, however incorrect. As a result, later editions of the *Shorter Oxford Dictionary* give 'parameter' its new meaning as well as the old ones.

Another debased word is 'algorithm.' My dictionary gives its meaning as 'The Arabic or decimal system of numeration; hence arithmetic', but medical journals use the word to mean a sort of diagrammatic summary of a disease.

One of the best ways of learning medicine is to be a patient in a general ward. There you will learn a lot about the human race and also about the problem of noise in hospitals. Members of the staff, lay but also nursing and even medical, not to mention the occasional patient, seem to delight in noise. They talk, shout, whistle, sing, clatter and bang things about. Some seem to think that working noisily indicates that they are working hard. Throughout my time working in hospitals I have collected the complaints of patients on the ground that if a complaint has any substance, something should be done about it. Four out of five complaints were about noise.

A curious medical cult is 'Osler worship.' I was taught by him and greatly admired him. He was undoubtedly a distinguished physician, a good teacher, a good writer and a character. He is commemorated by Osler Societies all over the world. Every large town in the United Kingdom has one, most of the States in the United States have one and, 70 years after his death, one has recently been founded in Japan. Why are there no Isaac Newton* societies or George Stephenson* or Isambard Kingdom Brunel* societies on the same worldwide scale?

Among the many problems of medical ethics is the question 'Should doctors always tell the truth?' If a patient asks 'Have I got cancer?' or 'Is my disease likely to be fatal?', plainly a doctor should tell the truth as far as possible, but there can be no hard and fast rules. He must decide what will be best for that particular patient and his family in those particular circumstances.

In 1990 surgeons in London operated on a baby with a congenital cardiac malformation while still in the mother's uterus. This received wide publicity and was hailed as a great advance. The baby died four days later. Had it lived it would have been permanently crippled, despite the operation. The operation consumed a great deal of medical time and talent, cost a lot of money and proved to be useless. Would the surgeons not have been better employed in shortening the hernia waiting list?

A constant cause of complaint about the medical profession is its use of vivisection in research. In my view, some is essential but there are often other means of obtaining the same result such as by using consenting medical students. Although I have held a vivisection licence and have practised vivisection, I have also used myself as an experimental animal: on one occasion I was rendered briefly unconscious fourteen times in one morning.

In 1941, when Howard Florey* had shown that penicillin cured infections in animals, he naturally wished to try it in human beings. He came to me and asked if he might administer it to some of my patients. I have strong views on experimenting on patients for whom I am personally responsible. I asked him: 'Have you tried it on yourself?' He replied he had not, so I said: 'If that is so, I regret that I cannot consent.' He then tried Sir Hugh Cairns. For various reasons he was unable to help. Florey next tried Leslie Witts. While they were discussing the matter, a young research assistant, Charles Fletcher, entered the room. Witts thought that this project would give him something to do. So Charles was the first person to show that penicillin was effective in humans, and naturally became quite famous. He later had a very distinguished career in medicine.

Another current problem is the rights and wrongs of experiments on embryos. Logically, the moment the spermatozoon has entered the ovum there is a potential human being. Just leave the thing alone and it will develop into a boy or a girl. There are no scientific grounds for saying that the first fourteen days do not count, or that it is only a collection of cells. You and I are only a collection of cells. Also the light-hearted destruction of embryos may deprive us of a future President of the Royal Society or, more seriously, of a future Mozart. On the other hand, I can appreciate the argument that experiments on a totally unwanted embryo might produce results of value to the human race.

CHAPTER TWELVE

Medical diagnosis

A correct diagnosis is an essential basis for rational treatment. Medicine is applied common sense, but also a strange mixture of the simple and the complex. Some of it could be understood by an intelligent nine-year-old, but some parts are extremely complicated and difficult. The ordinary textbook of medicine may describe a disease as having, say, five characteristic symptoms and five equally characteristic physical signs. One would think that, armed with these ten pieces of information, diagnosis would be simple. In real life some of the symptoms may be missing and others atypical, and this also applies to the physical signs. Moreover, in a case of any complexity there may be particularly misleading symptoms or signs that do not normally occur in this condition. The doctor is often required, in effect, to name a 200-piece jigsaw puzzle from the ten separate pieces that he has. The solution of these difficult problems is, in a mysterious and undefined way, aided by experience.

Mistakes and differences in opinion

Unfortunately, however much care is taken, mistakes are inevitable. A railway signalman of great experience, not tired, not worried, not drunk, in perfect health and concentrating on his job, may suddenly and inexplicably pull the wrong lever and wreck an express train. The same sort of thing can happen in medicine. How do such mistakes occur? Ignorance must be a possible factor, because medicine is such a vast subject that nobody can ever know it all. In real life most doctors know quite enough to deal with the common diseases but they may well be floored by some rarity described in Valparaiso in 1902 and still the only recorded example.

Most mistakes occur through errors of omission – not testing the urine, not looking down the throat, not asking patients whether and where they have been abroad, not doing a rectal examination, not looking at the hernial orifices, not taking the blood pressure and, commonest of all, not undressing the patient enough. I was once asked to see a patient with 'severe arthritis of the left shoulder', and would I arrange physiotherapy. I asked him to take his shirt off. He and his wife protested that it would be too painful. After much argument I cut his shirt off. He had a dislocated shoulder. Another patient had a sharp pain in the chest, thought to be pleurisy. When the clothes were removed, there was a patch of shingles.

Patients seldom deliberately give an untrue history, but may deceive the doctor by laying great stress on factors they think are important and leaving out others. Patients have been known to lead the doctor astray by not understanding Scottish, Welsh, American, Canadian, or Indian accents and being too polite to say so.

Medical mistakes are of two kinds: the blameworthy, where the doctor has broken the basic rules, and the blameless, where his procedure has been correct but he has misinterpreted the data. Many mistakes and accidents occur not through one factor but through a combination of them. An interesting and typical example occurred when I was knocked down by a motorcyclist outside my house. As I live in a very busy road where over 13,000 vehicles pass my house every day, I naturally exercise great caution when crossing the road. On this occasion, first, it was a dark night, second, the street lamp had gone out, third, I was wearing dark clothes (a dinner jacket) and fourth, I have a slight stoop. As a result, when I looked to the right to see if anything was coming, my nose obstructed the vision of my left eye (my better eye) and I have a large scotoma (blind spot) in the top half of my right field of vision. As a result I did not see the motorcyclist and stepped into the road. Also, I was not clearly visible to the girl riding the motorcycle. I received a cut scalp and since the accident have had an angular projection from my dorsal spine – I suspect a fracture. My wife was naturally concerned about the accident and suggested that I should go to bed and see a doctor. As it was the occasion of the Merton College Christmas dinner I declined to go to bed. As for seeing a doctor, I remarked that I had looked in the mirror and seen one, and he looked bloody awful. Patched up, I did go to the dinner.

As well as medical mistakes there are social mistakes, of which I have made my fair share. One, which fell into both classes, occurred on an occasion when my wife was about eight months pregnant. I said to a medical colleague: 'By Jove, our wives are having a neck and neck race.' It turned out that his wife was indeed pregnant, but only in her third month.

Mistakes are likely to lead to legal proceedings, and all prudent doctors belong to one of the defence organizations. When I joined the Medical Defence Union in 1924 the subscription was £3. It is now about £1,000. One branch of the profession at special risk is that of the obstetricians. If a baby is born with some defect, many of which are congenital or genetic, the average patient assumes that it is due to faulty obstetrical care. This is especially so in the United States where the legal system of no fee if the case is lost is a constant encouragement to litigation.

Observer error

An interesting parallel to ordinary mistakes is the teasing phenomenon of observer error, which has been known and studied for 30 years. In observer error there is no question of ignorance, carelessness or errors of omission. An experienced doctor, concentrating on his work and breaking no rules or medical principles, is still capable of making errors. I am grateful to Professor Charles Fletcher for the following examples:

• Five experienced clinicians recorded how far the liver edge was below the costal margin in 30 cases of hepatitis. Statistical examination of the results showed that they were randomly distributed.

• Four observers were asked to record the prevalence of sputum production in a group of patients. The results varied from 12 per cent to 42 per cent.

• Experienced radiologists were asked to report on a number of chest films as to whether or not they indicated certifiable pneumoconiosis. Needless to say they did not all agree. After an interval the procedure was repeated. As before, their opinions differed but they also differed from their own previous opinions. There were more differences related to smaller lesions. It was noteworthy that in a similar trial they did better if they worked in pairs. X-rays can be difficult to interpret because of over-exposure or under-exposure or because the patient is obese.

Another test of a particularly simple and straightforward nature was carried out by David Pyke* on finger clubbing. Twelve doctors and four medical students were asked to examine 12 patients and report whether a selected finger of each one was clubbed or not. They were not allowed to examine the patients in any other way or to question them. The observers were also shown photographs of the fingers in question and they were asked (without warning) to give their definition of finger clubbing. These varied greatly: more clubbing was reported from the bedside than from the photographs, probably because some patients were cyanosed or had an oxygen cylinder by the bed. The photograph of one such patient was held to show clubbing by only 10 of the 16 observers and in the case of a similar patient by only four. In general, the results varied from unanimity to equal division. Only one observer gave the same answers to clinical and photographic examination. I suppose one factor in observer error is the fact that more than one opinion can be held on most medical matters.

Euthanasia

My introduction to euthanasia occurred in 1924 when I was a house physician in the children's ward at St Thomas's Hospital. One of the most beautiful children that I have ever seen was slowly dying from tuberculous meningitis (for which there was then no treatment). The condition causes very severe headache for the child and agonising worry for the parents. The ward sister, a deeply religious woman, and I were horrified by the situation. She said: 'We *must* do something about this', so we jointly gave the child a large dose of morphia. This put an end to her sufferings and did something for the parents' distress. Technically our action was murder, but it seemed to us mere humanity.

Since then there has been much discussion on the matter and even suggestions that it should be regularized by Act of Parliament. I am against this. I could not bring myself to say: 'Right; I have filled in the form in triplicate, I have interviewed the two witnesses. I am busy today and am going out to lunch tomorrow so I will do it at four o'clock tomorrow afternoon.' Euthanasia is best left to the discretion and humanity of the doctor, always after consultation with the relatives. Also euthanasia must be used with great caution, because a fatal mistake would be a terrible disaster. I once saw in consultation an Oxford professor. He looked extremely unwell, and examination showed a very large, hard, craggy lump in the abdomen. To put it unscientifically, the tumour was nearly the size of a man's head. Any doctor would have given 500 to 1 that it was malignant. Fortunately we did not advise euthanasia. He lived for another twenty years and wrote two of his best books.

Confidentiality

Should patients be told all about their diagnosis and be allowed to read their notes? Often, even if they could understand the abbreviations and technical terms, and decipher the doctor's handwriting, they would not be much the wiser. Although it might calm the patient's fears, sometimes it would cause great distress and worry. The question of disclosure cannot be left to the doctor because if he refused, the average patient would at once assume bad news or that the doctor had made some mistake and was trying to conceal the fact. The best solution is probably to continue the present practice that the patient does not see his notes except for some special reason. Whatever my personal views may be, the situation has been altered by the Data Protection Act of 1984 and the Access to Health Records Act of 1990 which came into force on November 1st, 1991. Patients may not only examine their records but may ask for an explanation and for a photocopy.

Another problem is that in a small or single-handed practice the doctor knows all the patients socially and many are his friends. It is extremely difficult to diagnose and rationally treat people with whom one has an emotional relationship. Judgment is likely to be clouded. I have been summoned from my bed at three o'clock in the morning to see a doctor's wife whose husband thought that she was dying, to find nothing seriously wrong with her. Conversely, I have seen a doctor regarding his wife's illness with no serious concern when in fact she was dying. My advice to the newly-qualified has always been: 'Join a medical defence society and do not attempt to treat your own relations.'

Helping patients

It may be asked, 'How much good do doctors do?' In the preventive field they do a great deal – their advice on public health and factory Acts, their campaign against smoking, the introduction of preventive inoculation of children and for various tropical diseases, advice on diet, healthy living and hygiene are all vital. They have initiated clean water supply, inspection of food and the disposal of sewage. The advent of chemotherapy and antibiotics has given them powerful weapons. Hodgkin's disease and tuberculous meningitis, both invariably fatal when I was a student, are now curable. The childhood fevers have been conquered or abolished. Surgical advances have been great. In many diseases Nature does the cure – the doctor merely supports the patient psychologically.

How many times have I actually saved a life? By prompt tracheotomy three times; other occasions have been prompt diagnosis of meningitis, not forgetting to look down the throat in diphtheria, prompt treatment of diabetic coma, not forgetting to ask if the patient has been abroad, and where to, not forgetting to test the urine and, in severe alimentary bleeding, giving a massive blood transfusion. When examining female patients it is customary to pull the bedclothes down to just above the pubis. In a female patient with unexplained vomiting, which may have been attributed to food poisoning, it is essential to pull the bedclothes down further so as not to miss the strangulated femoral hernia. By these sorts of actions I estimate that I have saved about five lives a year. On a less dramatic level, I have helped many patients to have their illnesses in comfort.

Patients

Among many fortunate events in my life was the fact that on the day in 1932 that I was appointed to a consultant post I developed pneumonia. This illness taught me one thing – that patients are not merely people in bed for whom you have to do various things. They are fellow human beings having a bad time, mostly feeling very ill and probably worrying about the outcome. I have taken the patient's point of view ever since. All doctors, in whatever branch of clinical medicine they work, cannot avoid being psychiatrists, because all their patients have minds as well as bodies. I am often puzzled about psychiatry. Physicians and surgeons do their work in front of witnesses, whereas the psychiatrist is alone with his patient. How can he be assessed, say, for promotion or a professorial chair if the assessors have no information about his work or abilities, except perhaps by his publications, if any?

One of the charms of medicine is that no two patients are alike. Each has a unique set of genes, not to mention individual likes and dislikes, fears and prejudices, and widely differing environmental, ethnic, cultural and educational backgrounds. Though identical twins have the same genetic constitution they are not exactly the same. They have different fingerprints and pore prints. Even if two patients have exactly the same disease, their reactions to it may be entirely different. Another charm of the subject is that throughout your medical life at least once a week you learn some important new fact that you ought to have known years before.

Medicine can be hard work, not that that has ever harmed anybody. You must be prepared to stay up all night and do a full day's work next day. It can interfere with family life, having to cancel the theatre or a promised picnic. I once had to dash from Oxford to Banbury in the middle of Christmas dinner.

Doctors

It is good for doctors occasionally to be put in their place. In 1946 a Swiss medical organization arranged an Anglo-Swiss medical conference in Basel, I suspect less from a desire for medical cooperation than a desire to remind the British of the pleasures of Switzerland. The participants were put up in the *Drei Könige,* the best hotel in Basel, and given luxurious treatment. I had the good fortune to be one of those nominated to represent the University of Oxford on this occasion. I put on my best suit and my Anthony Eden hat and set out with a body of distinguished medical colleagues. When we reached Basel railway station, there was a scare about typhus fever, a relic of the recent war. It was ordained that one person in five, plus any suspicious-looking characters, should be deloused. To the delight of my colleagues I was one of those selected. I went in to what looked like a hospital and was asked to show my passport. I was immediately bowed out of the exit door. My medical colleagues of course asked me if I was itching less.

It was interesting to compare Switzerland with post-war Britain. The shops were brightly lit and full of luxury goods. The toilet paper in the hotel would have passed for the best writing paper in the United Kingdom, and on the shelves behind the hotel bar were 41 different kinds of alcoholic drinks.

One distinguished British participant, who should have known better and shall be nameless, had had his paper translated into German, a language of which he was totally ignorant. This, I thought, was not only unwise but looked like showing off. When the slides were upside down and he was asked questions in German he was defeated, and looked rather foolish.

On our return home I was made to pay the full duty on some presents that I had bought for my wife, while some people were not asked to pay anything on similar goods. I engaged the chairman of the Board of Customs and Excise in correspondence about this anomaly. He revealed that his officers were allowed to consider the apparent status of travellers. The moral is, to get through Customs quickly, wear your scruffiest clothes and have a crying child in tow.

CHAPTER THIRTEEN

Writing

I have always enjoyed writing. As a student I used to write would-be humorous articles in the Jesus College Magazine and the St Thomas's Hospital Gazette. Sir William Osler's *The Principles and Practice of Medicine* was then the most popular textbook in the English-speaking world. Apart from its technical merits it was embellished by numerous literary and historical references which intrigued and delighted his readers.

Like all medical students, I was an avid reader of the textbook, then in its tenth edition and discovered that in 1902 Dudgeon*, Mavrogordato* and Scott* had published 'An Examination Paper on Osler' in *St Thomas's Hospital Gazette.* Dudgeon became professor of pathology at St Thomas's and the other two also had distinguished careers. You will find their examination paper reproduced in Appendix 3.

I enjoy writing and it is difficult to stop

The paper caused widespread interest on both sides of the Atlantic, and Osler himself was delighted with it. Keen Oslerians soon added further questions and a version published in the *Annals of Internal Medicine* in 1973 included a total of 53 questions, as opposed to 35 in the original version.

In 1920, questions on Osler were still appearing in examination papers as is shown in an article by an unfortunate examinee published in that year's *King's College Gazette* which also included the questions he was expected to answer. (The article and questions appear in Appendix 4.)

My fellow students and I studied the 1902 and the 1920 examination papers and decided that the mine was not yet exhausted, so in 1927 two friends, Walter Chiesman* (later Sir Walter and Chief Medical Officer to the Treasury) and John Taylor (Pathologist to St George's Hospital) and I published a similar Examination Paper on Osler (10th edition) in the *St Thomas's Hospital Gazette*, with 43 questions and surprisingly little overlap as can be seen in Appendix 5. I have also written three books, have contributed to seven others and have written some 80 papers on medicine and the history of medicine, none of world-shaking importance. One fact of life is that there are not enough Nobel Prize type discoveries to go round. I enjoy writing, and it is difficult to stop. I must confess that now I prefer writing on the history of medicine rather than on modern medicine because the former does not change so rapidly as the latter.

My first book was a short biography of Sir Farquhar Buzzard, written at the request of his son Teddy*, a physician and a dear friend. Sir Farquhar had left remarkably few personal papers but had preserved hundreds and hundreds of newspaper cuttings about himself. This is a strange craft. Any of his remarks, even the most trivial, would be recorded in the London papers and in dozens of provincial papers all over the country. There were even cuttings from Sweden and one from Jerusalem. Who on earth scans the Jerusalem papers for the 1 in 50,000 chance of a reference to Buzzard, and if they do, who in the UK finds this out? I started on the book with enthusiasm but became bored with it. My wife said that I must finish it. Long experience has taught me never to argue with women because they have an annoying habit of being right, so I invited Teddy to lunch a fortnight later to receive the manuscript. I had it finished just in time.

My next work was to write Volume 3 of *A History of the Royal College of Physicians of London*. The first two volumes had been written by Sir George Clark*, an eminent professional historian. My contacts with him were a source of great pleasure. As well as vast learning in history and many other subjects, all borne with modesty and humour, he had an extraordinary fund of general knowledge on all subjects. For example, we were once talking about doctors who took to literature and naturally Chekhov was mentioned. I remarked that unlike most literary doctors he continued to practise medicine. George said: 'Yes, his stethoscope is preserved in the museum at Yalta in the Crimea.'

Sir George took the narrative from 1518 up to 1858. My volume went from the Medical Act of 1858 to the National Health Act of 1948. I found it a fascinating task, although it was what is known in criminal circles as 'four years hard labour.' The chief trouble in this period is the vast amount of material. I had to slog through 160 volumes of *The Lancet* and the *British Medical Journal* for the general medical background and references to the College, 90 volumes of the General Medical Council minutes and 37 volumes of the College Annals, comprising some 11,000 pages, not to mention reports of Royal Commissions and Select Committees, White Papers, Bills, Acts of Parliament and Hansard. For personal details Munk's *Roll of the College* and the *Dictionary of National Biography* provided ample material. The College Annals were mostly in manuscript and, fortunately, written in legible Victorian handwriting.

Shortly before the book was published my wife and I were invited to spend a weekend with Lord and Lady Moran* at their country house, I have always supposed so that he could find out what I had written about him. I did not reveal this but I had in fact praised him because he was a successful President and did a great deal for the College and medicine. The Morans were most hospitable and my wife enjoyed sleeping in a 17th century bed with a long box at the foot in which to put her sword.

In one respect Lady Moran was unique. A few years earlier she had had a stroke which rendered her completely unconscious. As the weeks and months went by, the doctors gave a hopeless prognosis. After one year she woke up and was normal. It is true that she walked with a stick but her mental functions were perfect.

In the garage I found a number of papers, some eaten by mice. With Moran's permission I went through them and found some interesting material which I put in the book. The prize item was a sheet of paper headed 'Those on my side and those against.' It was fascinating reading, but too inflammable to publish. The volume appeared in 1972.

I next undertook, for the Royal Society of Medicine, the revision and adaptation for the British market of the *Family Medical Guide,* a popular American book for the intelligent layman. One might think that the two countries spoke the same language but the differences in terminology, the actual diseases found in the two countries and the different attitudes to disease were surprising, not to mention the changes that occur in some parts of medicine even in a few years. As a result some chapters had to be rewritten while others could remain unchanged. The book appeared in 1980.

In 1991 I wrote an autobiography for my children and grandchildren under the title *The Cooke's Tale*. My family suggested that I should expand its medical content for a wider readership, and it is as a result of their persuasion that I completed this volume.

CHAPTER FOURTEEN

Orthodox medicine and alternative medicine

The name Harley Street has a universal appeal to the layman. It is, of course, a London postal address and not a qualification. The street does contain many distinguished practitioners but also some nonentities. Any medically qualified person can set up in business there. A few years ago there were in the Oxford area two very ordinary general practitioners who each rented a room in Harley Street for one afternoon a week. They seldom went there, but wrote all their letters on Harley Street notepaper. Their Oxford patients used to say with obvious pride 'My doctor is a Harley Street man.'

When I was on the General Medical Council we had a case of two general practitioners who set up a slimming clinic in Harley Street. The patients had little history taken and no physical examination. They were charged a large fee and given three remedies: an anti-appetite pill, a diuretic and a purgative. On the way home they had to hurry into the toilet several times. On reaching home they were delighted to find that they had already lost several pounds in weight.

The Medical Act of 1858 lays down that no doctor can be compelled to follow any particular line of treatment, which opens the door to any kind of eccentricity or even quackery. Many years ago there was a small-pox epidemic in Gloucester. A general practitioner, Dr Hadwen, did not believe in vaccination and refused to vaccinate any of his child patients. As a result several died and he was prosecuted. He was acquitted because under the Medical Acts he could not be compelled to believe in the efficacy of vaccination.

It is not often recognized by laymen that there are few bars to their practising medicine. The preamble to the Medical Act states simply that 'Whereas it is expedient that persons requiring medical aid shall be enabled to distinguish qualified from unqualified practitioners . . . '

There have been many attempts to limit medical practice to those legally qualified, but Parliament has always rejected them, partly because of the layman's common regard for unorthodox methods of treatment, and partly from a belief in Bernard Shaw's dictum that 'all professions are a conspiracy against the layman'. As a result, in theory any layman may perform a heart transplant provided he does not pretend to be a medical man. On the other hand, he may not serve in any public medical service, such as with the armed forces, attend a woman in childbirth except in emergency, treat venereal disease or practise dentistry. As regards the last, every doctor is a qualified dentist because he is entitled to treat every part of the human body. The Veterinary Acts are stricter: an experienced surgeon may not legally perform a minor operation on his own dog.

Alternative or fringe medicine

There is great public interest in these methods of diagnosis and treatment, fostered by frequent references to them in the media and by royal patronage. Methods of diagnosis include closing the eyes and examining the patient's aura, swinging a pendulum over the patient's body, studying only the iris, studying only the big toe, kineseology, hair analysis or by not examining the patient at all – diagnosis by divination. These may sound improbable, but I have seen most of them in action. There is a wide choice in methods of treatment, including homoeopathy, faith healing, osteopathy, hypnotherapy, shiatsu, meditation, chiropractice, acupuncture, vertebral therapy, Christian Science, aromatherapy, mesotherapy, hypnosis, reflexology, herbalism, naturopathy, yoga, bone setting, hydrotherapy, inhaling various gases (including the breath of a cow or a virgin), radiaesthesia, relaxation, immersion in sand, mud, hot water or cold water, exposure to coloured lights, injection of 1 ml of the patient's own urine under the skin, and many others.

An interesting example appeared on television recently – a woman in a white coat, looking very clinical, was examining a man lying on a couch. He was fully dressed except for bare feet. The woman carefully moved his big toe up and down and eventually pronounced: 'Yes, you have got nasal sinusitis.'

The exponents of each method regard theirs as the best and the others as less effective, if not useless. The methods vary so enormously that it is difficult to believe that they can all be right. The basis of any rational treatment is a firm diagnosis but most of these systems have very little to say about this aspect. They concentrate on treatment. There is no doubt that patients are cured, or at least recover, by means of these unorthodox methods. One reason is that of all human ailments few are fatal and the majority get better anyhow, a fact as important for fringe medicine as for orthodox medicine. Another reason is that every disease, major or minor, has a psychological element because every patient has a mind as well as a body. Patients like an enthusiastic healer who offers an immediate and confident diagnosis and an even more confident cure, and are always impressed by the unusual. If you have faith in your healer, you recover more quickly. A third reason is that on the whole the alternative therapists do not treat serious diseases. It is very unlikely that an aromatherapist would undertake the treatment of a compound fracture of the femur, or a hypnotist that of meningococcal meningitis.

When homoeopathy was introduced in about 1800 it undoubtedly did good because the fashion then was to prescribe enormous amounts of drugs. It is a curious system of healing by reason of its belief that the more dilute a medicine the more powerful its effect. With the highest 'potencies' the patient is lucky to receive a single molecule of the drug and is in fact receiving only tap water, but as Samuel Hahnemann*, the founder, said it is how the medicine is given that matters. Another curious fact is that if homoeopathy is so superior to orthodox medicine, why, after nearly 200 years, has it not long since taken its place?

I happen to know something about Christian Science because many of my wife's family were of this faith. Two of them died after long and painful illnesses which could easily have been cured by orthodox medicine. I know of no evidence that Christian Scientists live longer than other people. When patients die in a Christian Science nursing home there is no doctor to issue a death certificate, so there has to be a postmortem examination and a coroner's inquest. In the case of my sister-in-law I wrote to the coroner and obtained a copy of the postmortem report. This unfortunate woman had a carcinoma of the breast which over a period of many months had spread to the other breast and had eaten its way through the chest wall into the lung. No drugs were used, and the patient's husband (of the same faith) reported that when the pain was very severe the nurse sang her a hymn. My wife was not allowed to visit her dying sister because she was married to a doctor and so might introduce harmful medical influences. So much for a religion based on Christianity and kindness. This lady's husband later came under my care, dying from uraemia due to untreated prostatism. We were not able to save him. I later learnt that the Christian Science view was: 'Of course he died, because he left Christian Science care and went into a hospital.'

One of the criticisms often aimed at unorthodox medicine is that it does not go in much for controls. The same failing sometimes occurs in orthodox medicine. There was a well-known surgeon who devised an unorthodox method of treatment which was regarded with general disapproval by his colleagues. When asked if he had used any controls he replied: 'No, my registrar was far too busy interviewing satisfied patients.'

Doctors also achieve success by new and sometimes unorthodox methods. A modern example is holistic medicine, that is, looking at the patient as a whole and not only at the diseased part. It is claimed as a new and modern discovery, but I was taught this as a student in the 1920s and practised it for over 60 years. Fortunately, early in my career I learnt that I was treating not diseases but human beings.

My preference for orthodox medicine derives from the fact that it has a sound scientific background. The bodily functions and their disturbances in disease have been measured, analysed, weighed, counted and tested in great detail and also fit in with the principles of accepted scientific thought. On the other hand it can be logically argued that if the patient recovers, the nature of the treatment does not matter. Unorthodox practitioners do not always get it right and I have seen some grim and tragic examples of their errors.

Quackery

The more extreme forms of unorthodox medicine merge into quackery, which has always existed and always will exist. The successful quack requires personality, powers of oratory, boundless self-confidence and no scruples. The first thing the quack does is to frighten the patient. A notable quack, James Graham (1745–1794) used to do so by diagnosing, for example, hockogrockles, marthambles, the moon pall, the strong fives, glimmering of the gizzard, quavering of the kidney, or the wambling trot. His remedies, which guaranteed immediate cure, also had impressive names – Sovereign Julep, Vatican Pills, Incomparable Balsam, Tincture of the Sun, Divine Baths of Reformation, the Royal Decoction, the Electuary Balm of Gilead, Great Cordial Antidote, Panchimagogum, Lady Moor's Drops or Pilula Salutiferens.

In 1760 he opened his Temple of Health in the newly-built Adelphi Terrace in London. To illustrate health and encourage customers he displayed a beautiful young girl wearing very little clothing, who was later known to posterity as Emma Hamilton*. A feature of the Temple of Health was the enormous Celestial Bed, resting on glass pillars and accompanied by music, scents and doves. Infertile couples paid large sums to hire the bed for one night. Despite all this Graham went bankrupt. Not discouraged, he then started cures by earth, in which the patients were buried in earth with only their heads showing above the ground, looking like a row of cabbages.

Quacks often have great success. Patients go to them from disappointment with orthodox medicine – especially when given bad news or told that there is no cure – love of the dramatic or the unknown, a desire for secrecy, fashion or even sheer curiosity. One of the strangest forms of what I regard as quackery is based on the belief that the planets all take a personal interest in my private affairs.

Quacks also occur in the medical profession, although their success may be brief. Dr Émile Coué (1857–1926) was the apostle of autosuggestion. His slogan 'Tous les jours, à tous points de vue, je vais de mieux en mieux' ('Every day in every way I am getting better and better') swept the civilized world, but after his death was forgotten in a few months.

Elisha Perkins (1741–1799), an American, became rich and famous from his metallic tractors. These were rods three inches long made of a strip of iron and one of brass stuck together, costing one shilling to make and sold for five guineas. If the tractors were drawn along the body *in the right direction* the disease was cured. A sceptical colleague obtained the same results with wooden tractors painted to look like metal.

The *British Medical Journal* in May 1989 carried an account of a medically-qualified quack who charged a fee of £10,000 for a completely useless remedy for AIDS. It is amazing how otherwise sensible and apparently rational people are deceived by quackery. In the 18th century the British Parliament voted £5,000 to buy the formula of a remedy for bladder stones, consisting of powdered snails, carrot seed, burdock and hawthorn, all to be burnt black and then mixed with soap and honey.

Medical practice I

A curious medical incident occurred in my family in 1868. My father, aged 16, went to sea as an apprentice in a four-masted sailing ship, the *Salisbury*. One of the sailors had a swelling in the scrotum. The ship's captain consulted his manual and decided that it was a hernia. The treatment advised was to push the swelling back into the abdomen. This was tried, with vigour but without success.

The next manoeuvre advised was to put the patient in a hot bath and repeat the process. There were of course no hot baths in such sailing ships, but sailors are resourceful men. The ship's carpenter rigged up a canvas bath which was filled with hot water and the unfortunate patient submitted to the attempts of his most muscular shipmates to reduce the hernia. These too failed. The last procedure advised was to make the patient unconscious by inflating the rectum with tobacco smoke. The ship's carpenter got to work again, but before he had completed the apparatus the ship reached Karachi. A doctor diagnosed the swelling as a hydrocele (an abnormal collection of fluid round the testicle), which should certainly not be pushed back into the abdomen.

When I was a small boy I had bad chilblains on my toes, partly due to tight shoes. Rapidly-growing children require new shoes at least three times a year but I suspect that my parents could not afford such luxury. I can remember painfully tight shoes and I still have some deformed and overlapping toes. The chilblains were cured by my wearing sandals over bare feet. My parents were loudly criticized by passers-by for allowing a poor child to go about with bare feet in midwinter, but it was an immediate and permanent cure.

Medicine is a wonderful subject. Like chess it has no limits and also provides a good general education – in chemistry, physics, botany, zoology, anatomy, physiology, pathology and psychology, in fact about people. One of the first things one learns is the truth of the Yorkshire saying 'There's nowt so queer as folk.'

Consulting practice episodes

When I began consulting medical practice in 1933 I had to provide myself with the necessary equipment. I went into collusion with an old friend, later Sir Walter Chiesman, Chief Medical Officer to the Treasury, and we designed the ultimate consultant's outfit. There were two cases. The smaller one (17in × 10in × 6in) contained stethoscope, sphygmomanometer, ophthalmoscope, auriscope, knee hammer, tuning fork, tape measure, spatulas, finger stalls and vaseline, pharmacopoeia, notes on tropical diseases and a writing block.

The larger (about 21in × 14in × 9in) contained a sterilizer, apparatus for tapping the chest or abdomen, lumbar puncture, sigmoidoscopy, tracheotomy (adult and child), urine testing, passing catheter and stomach tube, containers for collecting samples of blood, urine, faeces, vomit or food, sutures, and emergency remedies. It was not only large but weighed over 30lb, so when I had to carry it into a house I sometimes felt that I must look like a man selling vacuum cleaners. Over the years everything in the smaller case was used many times and almost everything in the larger case, including the adult tracheotomy set, which I was able to lend to an ENT surgeon in an emergency. The larger case is now in the Oxfordshire Health Authority archives.

I had had no experience of consulting practice and had a lot to learn. Apart from a terrifying fortnight in general practice (described in Chapter 4) I had worked only in hospitals. My ignorance was soon revealed when I entered a patient's bedroom in front of the general practitioner and received a stern and well-deserved rebuke. The patient's own doctor should, of course, enter first and introduce the consultant, and the patient should not be frightened by a strange man entering the bedroom.

There have been other embarrassing occasions such as when a general practitioner (a pillar of the establishment) appeared to be very drunk. He could hardly stand up or speak coherently. It was plain that he could not manage the stairs, so I suggested that he sat down and rested while I looked at the patient. He agreed. When I came down he was perfectly well. The cause was severe migraine.

Another embarrassing occasion of a different kind was when the patient's doctor and I entered a bedroom to find in a double bed an elderly man and wife. He was talking to her and holding her hand, but she was dead. All our tact was required.

There is in chest medicine a physical sign, 'the cracked pot sound.' It sounds better in French, *le bruit de pot fêlé*. On one occasion as I approached the patient's bed I inadvertently kicked the chamber pot just under it – *le bruit de pot non-fêlé*. The patient was embarrassed, but the pot provided the diagnosis. The patient was severely dehydrated, but the urine was pale, so the reason was renal failure.

One satisfactory occasion was when a foolish mistake saved the patient's life. A boy of 10 was returning with his parents from the Far East. During the voyage he developed high fever and looked very ill. There happened to be several doctors in the ship, including two malarialogists, none of whom could suggest a diagnosis. The boy looked so ill that he was landed at Marseille and put in hospital. The French doctors could not help so he was taken on board again, and eventually arrived in London under the care of a friend of mine. I was asked to see the boy, with the cheerful words 'Here is a puzzle for you.' The boy had a high temperature and a palpable spleen and looked extremely ill. I too was puzzled. I made a blood film and saw some very abnormal cells. I thought that he must have leukaemia. There was then no treatment for this condition, so before breaking the dreadful news to the parents I thought that I had better find out what type it was, because it might have some bearing on how long he was likely to live. I took the blood film to a pathologist who said: 'You ass, your abnormal cells are malarial parasites.' I had never seen a malarial parasite before – so much for medical education! The boy was cured in a week.

Malaria is an extraordinary disease. At this moment there are millions of people suffering from it. It is probably the commonest disease. It has been found in Russia as far north as latitude 60°, which is about the level of the Shetland Isles. It is one of the most protean diseases. As one expert said: 'It can imitate any medical condition except pregnancy and gonorrhoea, and you can't really be sure about these.' At present malaria is a serious problem because some types have developed resistance to the usual remedies. I have seen a patient in Oxford with malaria who had never been abroad. His father had recently had malaria, and there are anopheline mosquitos in this country ready to transmit it.

A totally different problem is the social relationship between the consultants and the general practitioners. They often meet, get to know each other well and naturally often become friends. If they dine together, is this a social occasion or is the consultant seeking business? In my experience common sense has prevailed in this matter.

How does the public regard doctors? They are much in the public eye, because of frequent references in the press to events of medical interest, and the too frequent references to 'We are on the verge of a breakthrough.' A doctor committing a crime is always news. Reporting of the proceedings of the General Medical Council, especially if scandalous or sexual, is always popular, as are unusual or dramatic operations. In private life grateful patients talk about their doctors – dissatisfied patients even more so. Doctors in literature usually come out well. Over all we do not do badly.

I have always fought against what I call 'corridor medicine', that is when you are walking down a corridor and someone accosts you and asks for medical advice. My reply always is: 'If you wish to consult me, come to my rooms where I will take a full history and give you a proper examination.' Corridor medicine can be dangerous.

In January 1960 I received a subpoena to attend a divorce case. The wife was a young woman doctor whom I had seen as a patient. Her husband, out of spite, claimed to be domiciled in Scotland so the whole proceedings were removed to Edinburgh. It could not have been more inconvenient. The weather was freezing, I was very busy, I had to give up several important engagements. I was naturally furious and proposed to take my revenge by giving evidence the opposite way to what was expected. In the event, the sight of this beautiful and tear-stained girl made me relent, but to add insult to injury I had to take legal action to obtain my fee and expenses.

Hospital consultant practice

My main duty in the hospital was looking after the patients, but I greatly enjoyed my other duty of teaching the students. My lecture-demonstrations to the preclinical students have already been described. There was also the teaching of clinical students in the wards. This was enjoyable because they all were keen to learn, unlike some schoolchildren who actively resist instruction.

I always asked my new ward clerks two general knowledge questions. The first, what does the National Health Service cost, and the second, what is the normal number of teeth. I never received a correct answer to either question. To the second the figure given was not always divisible by four, and on one memorable occasion not divisible by two. What had they been learning in the anatomy department?

I was given to using slogans, proverbs and medical aphorisms, which came to be known as Cooke's Laws, such as:

It always takes longer than you think it will.

It always costs more than you think it will.

However distinguished the medical staff of a hospital, the most important person in it is the patient.

We have professors like other people have mice.

The best surgeon is the one who knows when not to operate.

The less useful the department, the greater its demands for space, staff and money.

Seven deadly sins may be enough for the theologian, but there are many more in medicine.

Never have a garden bigger than your wife can manage.

A lecture is the process by which information is transferred from the notebook of the lecturer to the notebook of the student without passing through the mind of either (Leacock).

Before you try some new procedure on a patient ask yourself: 'Would I like this done to myself, my wife or my child?'

A good way of learning medicine is to be ill and experience it from the receiving end.

There are only two economic laws:

1. Your prediction will be wrong.
2. It will cost more than you ever thought possible.

A registrar can do all the things that his chief does, only better.

Listen to what the patient is saying, he is probably telling you the answer.

Twice the correct dose of a medicine does not do twice as much good.

Remember, you are not treating diseases, you are treating human beings.

The commonest diseases occur most often. (The American version of the last aphorism is: If you hear hoof-beats, do not say zebras.)

Research should be pronounced REsearch because most of it has been done before.

Protect the patients from being 'technology fodder'.

Doctors pour drugs about which they know little into bodies about which they know less (Voltaire).

Minor operations are those had by other people.

At Henley Royal Regatta the size of the Leander cap is in inverse proportion to the square of the girth.

When I retired my pupils talked of publishing Cooke's Laws. To my great relief they did not, because very few are original.

Junior colleagues

I have had six registrars. All have had distinguished careers: Denis Lewin in 1947 (died 1985); John Pease in 1949, physician at Mansfield; David

Pyke in 1952, who was a physician to King's College Hospital where he ran the Diabetic Clinic, and was for many years Registrar of the Royal College of Physicians of London; next came Gerald Honey in 1957, a physician in Liverpool; and in 1961 Francis Caird, now professor of geriatric medicine at Glasgow University. My last registrar was a delightful and apparently balanced man with a charming wife and family who, after I had retired, to my amazement and distress committed suicide.

I have had sixty-seven house physicians, of whom at least forty-six have become consultants. One was killed mountaineering. The one whom I regarded as the best that I had ever had died in Uganda from some tropical disease. The most interesting was Roger Ormrod. From Shrewsbury School he came up to the Queen's College, Oxford, to read medicine. He found anatomy boring and changed to reading law. He practised as a barrister in London until the 1939 war and then qualified in medicine. He was my house physician in 1942, then joined the Royal Army Medical Corps and became an assistant director of medical services. After the war he returned to the Bar, became a Queen's Counsel, then a High Court judge and ended as a Lord Justice of Appeal and a Privy Councillor. It was he who persuaded the lawyers to believe in blood groups in paternity cases. A most delightful companion, he died in 1992.

Of other house physicians, George Alberti is Professor of Medicine at Newcastle; Tom Stapleton became Professor of Child Health at Sydney University, Australia; Oliver Wrong was Professor of Medicine at Dundee and then Professor of Medicine at London University, based at University College Hospital, London.

Medical miscellani

My colleague Fred Hobson, a man of great energy and an enthusiast for preventive medicine, decided to take serum from adults who had had measles and use it to protect children for whom it might be dangerous to have this disease. Collecting the serum was easy, but it had to be processed and put into glass containers so that it could be kept until needed. This was done by a well-known drug firm, who by mistake or carelessness or by deliberately cheating, instead of processing the Oxford serum simply bottled mixed adult serum. This is a sure way of spreading hepatitis, and indeed that is just what happened. Four, but not all, of the children who were given the serum developed fulminating hepatitis and died in a few days.

Sections of the liver of one victim showed only a pink blur with no evidence of liver structure. We reported these events to the Ministry of

Health and some enquiries were made. It had happened before but had been forgotten about. No one sued the drug firm, as they should have done.

The episode was a complete puzzle to the practitioners and myself, so we sought the help of Lord Dawson of Penn. He too had never seen the like before, but he helped in several ways. He looked at me and said: 'Cooke, when were you last in bed?' I owned up that I had been up for the previous night. He asked for the name of my house physician and introduced him to the parents as a distinguished physician who would be in charge, and I was sent off to bed.

The mother of two of the children, who were obviously dying, was understandably distraught and became very drunk. She went up to Dawson and screamed: 'Why are these children vomiting blood?' Dawson slowly patted his own abdomen twice and said: 'It's the stomach.' She was satisfied.

When examining patients one tends to get into a routine. On countless occasions I have said to a female patient: 'Please take everything off except your knickers.' One one occasion I was saying this to a very fat lady and suddenly heard myself say: 'Please take everything off except your stomach'. The subconscious can be a nuisance. Fortunately she was not listening. Talking of examining patients, I have never made a rectal or vaginal examination in a woman without explaining the why and the wherefore and having a female witness present. Failure to do this can have disastrous results. Also on the subject of examination, it is rare for female patients, even nuns, to show embarrassment at physical examination. I have met very few examples.

On an unusual and delightful occasion a child of two, when undressed, brushed her hands over her nipples and navel and said: 'My spots, they'll soon be gone.' Occasionally young girls with developing breasts are embarrassed. The strangest incidents were on three occasions when elderly married women with children showed excessive modesty at uncovering their breasts. In each case the reason was that they were concealing a large scirrhus carcinoma.

I was once travelling in a train from London to Oxford when a woman in the carriage started wheezing. As there was another passenger in the carriage who knew that I was a doctor, I felt that I ought to help, so I said to the woman: 'Excuse me, madam, but is your trouble asthma?' She replied that it was. I said that I was a doctor and perhaps could help. I asked her if she carried any remedy, and she produced some very large tablets.

As it would obviously be impossible to swallow them dry, I went along to the toilet to get some water, but there was no vessel to put it in. The only thing to do was to take her along to the toilet and put some water in my cupped hands so that she could swallow her tablets. The moment we entered she shut the door and began to undress. I was horrified. I pictured the letter from the General Medical Council and the headlines in the local newspaper. I felt that I could not leave her untreated so, while she waved her breasts at me, I managed to get the tablets down, and then ran for it. She later returned to the carriage, dressed I am glad to say, and the asthma better. She was obviously very drunk and to my relief got out at Didcot.

Do you remember your patients? The answer is: 'Not all, but some, such as the lady in the train, can never be forgotten.' One difficulty is that you may see a woman in hospital who is wearing no make-up and her hair looks like a bird's nest. Three months later you meet her at a sherry party in her full war paint and she thinks you stupid or ill-mannered for not recognizing her. There were other patients whom I can never forget. One was a girl in St Thomas's with anorexia nervosa. She said that the only thing that she would eat was fried bacon. The hospital kitchen rallied round and each day the most delicious fried bacon was served, eagerly received by the girl and disappeared. We were pleased at this until we discovered that she was still losing weight. The mystery was solved when the hospital librarian asked why so many patients were using rashers of bacon as bookmarks in the library books.

Another was a charming old gentleman in a nursing home who for good reasons had a nasal tube, a drainage tube in the abdomen and an indwelling catheter. He woke in the night a bit muddled and in discomfort. A keen gardener, he managed to find his pruning knife and cut off all three tubes flush with the skin.

An interesting patient was a girl who said that she was not passing any urine. Day after day she produced no urine. As she remained perfectly well and had a normal blood urea we knew that there must be a catch about it. The reason turned out to be that she had told the ward sister that she had a sore bottom and had persuaded her to let her have a water bed. We soon found that the water bed contained dilute urine. How did it get there? A water bed is a flat rubber bag the size of a bed. It is filled from an orifice at one corner, about one inch across and closed by a screw plug. How the girl managed to urinate through this small hole without spilling any was a remarkable gymnastic feat.

Before the days of antibiotics I once saw a bishop, seriously ill with pneumonia. There was great ecclesiastical and family concern, so we decided to ask Lord Horder* to see him. When the patient was told this, he said in a feeble voice: 'Do you think that he might buy my palace?' Horder came and carefully examined the patient. When we adjourned next door to hear his opinion, he looked out of the window and said: 'That's a nice magnolia.' We had twenty minutes on the care of magnolias and five minutes on the bishop – who did recover.

One of the charms of medicine is the unexpected. My house physician once rang me up to say that he had admitted a doctor with tetanus. I remarked that this was an unlikely disease for a medical man. The house physician said that the patient's jaw was tightly closed and added that he had bitten his tongue. I replied that he had not got tetanus because in that condition he could not have opened his mouth enough to have put his tongue out. I went to have a look at him. He was not able to give a history. On examination his jaw was indeed tightly shut and he seemed generally unwell. The only other finding was that his abdominal wall looked like a relief map of the Alps from hundreds of injections that had been given without aseptic technique. We eventually discovered that he was given to alcohol and drugs. On the present occasion he had got very drunk, had tried to inject morphia but by mistake had injected strychnine. Despite these failings, when he died some years later he had a glowing obituary and his patients founded a memorial to this much loved doctor.

CHAPTER SIXTEEN

Medical practice II

As well as technical knowledge, medicine requires common sense. I once had under my care a man with severe hypertension at the time when pressure-reducing drugs had just come in, and naturally we were using them with extreme caution. When he was discharged I wrote to his doctor in London outlining the treatment, and suggesting that it would be wise to take the blood pressure every two or three hours during the day. I had failed to notice that the doctor lived in Bayswater and the patient in The Temple. I received a charming but sarcastic letter pointing out that to go from Bayswater to the Temple and back say six times a day through London's traffic would take up the whole day.

About 1936 it occurred to me that it might be feasible and even useful to insert a small telescope through the abdominal wall and inspect the viscera. It turned out not to be a new idea. Someone had done it in the 1890s. In 1937 I went to Berlin to study laparoscopy in the clinic of Heinz Kalk, and acquired the apparatus. (Incidentally, in Berlin, two years before World War II, there were twice-weekly air raid rehearsals.) I then did a number of laparoscopies, some of which were of diagnostic value and some of which saved the patient from having a laparotomy. The procedure is now common and has been extended to operative laparoscopy.

In 1939 two of our children developed whooping cough. Life was simpler then. We just telephoned the Hospital for Sick Children at Great Ormond Street in London. A day nurse and a night nurse came down on the next train. It is important to manage this disease the right way. Like all diseases, whooping cough has a psychological component. The poor child coughs and coughs until it is black in the face, whoops and is then sick. Its sufferings naturally distress the parents. If they show much sympathy, it prolongs the illness. They must harden their hearts and, however they feel, *show* no sympathy. They should even discourage the child from coughing. These manoeuvres will greatly shorten the illness.

Another of our children had whooping cough at the time of a birthday. One present was her first bicycle, which was brought to the sick room to be admired. When she had recovered she went to stay with an aunt at Bournemouth for a fortnight's convalescence. On her return home, perfectly well, she ran into the garden and saw the bicycle. She immediately had a paroxysm of coughing, whooped and vomited.

Luckily, a special providence watches over children. One of ours was waving a stick about and by accident hit her little brother in the eye. There were loud cries so I went to see what had happened. To my dismay I saw a deep groove across one cornea, which would have seriously impaired vision. I was about to take him to the eye hospital when the groove sprang out and restored the normal contour.

The epidemiology of diseases is a fascinating but obscure subject. In my professional lifetime duodenal ulcer has appeared, become common and has now almost disappeared. In my youth, scarlet fever was a common and serious disease for which patients were always admitted to a fever hospital. It has disappeared. Measles in those days was a minor disease but is now more dangerous. In a recent number of the *Proceedings of the Royal Society of Medicine* it was pointed out that in 1930 deaths from cancer of the stomach were nine times as common as deaths from cancer of the lung; that ratio is now reversed. Fashions in investigations have also changed. Very few fractional test meals are done now, and few doctors have ever heard of the opsonic index.

A few years ago smallpox was eradicated from the world, the most remarkable feat of public health and preventive medicine ever carried out. There was scarcely any mention in the media of this astounding event. I suppose that if a couple of cases had occurred in Brixton that would have been headline news.

In 1936 Professor J. S. Haldane*, an eminent physiologist, died. His son, Jack Haldane*, also a scientist, expressed a wish that his father's brain, certainly a distinguished one, should be examined. I happened to know that Dr Donaldson of the Wistar Institute in the United States had written a paper on the brains of three scholars, one of whom was Sir William Osler, which he had compared with those of three illiterate garbage men. He made a most minute examination, cutting thousands of sections, and counting innumerable cells. As anybody could have told him, all six brains were almost exactly the same. Nevertheless, Jack Haldane still wished his father's brain to go to Donaldson, who agreed to receive it.

If ever you feel like sending a brain to the United States my advice is DON'T. By the time I had satisfied the public health authorities on both sides of the Atlantic, the shipping line and the transporting agents, each of whom insisted on a different kind of packing, including a sealed metal box, six inches of sawdust all round and a reinforced container, we ended with a cube of nearly three feet each way. It cost quite a lot and I had to pay. About ten years later I wrote to Dr Donaldson to ask how he was getting on with the examination. He replied that he had been rather busy and had not started yet.

Jack Haldane, perhaps to repay me for my trouble and expense, invited me to dine in New College, my first visit to the High Table of an Oxford College. I was seated next to the famous warden William Spooner, but he did not make any 'spoonerisms' on that occasion. The truth is that in fact he made only one spoonerism when he gave out a hymn as 'Kinkering congs their titles take from the captives that they make.'

Most of the well-known 'spoonerisms' are the work of ingenious New College undergraduates – such as 'You have hissed all my mystery lectures. In fact you have tasted a whole worm. You will leave Oxford by the town drain.' There is also said to have been a practical one. When seeing his wife off by train, when the whistle blew, he thrust sixpence into his wife's hand and kissed the porter goodbye. It is also alleged that he told one of his housemaids to be sure that some letters should catch the evening post. Next morning they were still on the hall table. Very annoyed, he summoned the two maids and said: 'Which of you two girls pissed the most last night?' All this is very unfair because he was an excellent warden. He had a family and I knew one of his daughters, Rosemary.

On a more cheerful theme, Harold Burn, professor of pharmacology at Oxford and a good friend of mine, was often asked to lecture in the United States. On one of these occasions a visitor to his department asked one of his research assistants how the department got on when the professor was away. The reply was: 'Oh, we just fiddle while Burn roams.'

On another occasion an Oxford professor, who had better be nameless, and who although highly intelligent was a simple man, attended a dinner given to Russian delegates visiting Oxford. He sat next to the wife of one of his junior colleagues. She was a striking young woman, wearing black with a plunging neck line and looking the typical *femme fatale*. He had never seen anything like this before and assumed that she must be a Russian, so he talked to her in pidgin English.

Before the National Health Service, Oxford had a regional hospital board which supervised the local hospitals. Its chairman was Sir Farquhar Buzzard, the Regius Professor of Medicine. It came to the board's knowledge that at the Thame Cottage Hospital the only documentation of the patients was a temperature chart. There were no notes or treatment sheets. The treatments existed only in the matron's memory, so if she had a day off nobody received any medicine. The board wrote to those local practitioners who used the hospital and suggested that they held a meeting to arrange some much needed improvements. Unfortunately, this was not possible because none of them was on speaking terms with any of the others.

Buzzard therefore suggested that I should pay a monthly visit to the hospital to try to institute improvements and see that they were carried out. I did not relish this assignment, but said that I would do it. A date was fixed for my first visit. On that day, at 5.30 in the morning, I was asked to see a patient urgently in the Thame area, so I threw my clothes on over my pyjamas and dashed off. The patient turned out to be a little boy with acute meningitis. By the time he had had a lumbar puncture and arrangements had been made for his transfer to the Radcliffe Infirmary, it was time for breakfast. After that there was no time for me to go home, complete my toilet and return to Thame in time for the meeting. So, unwashed, unshaved, and wearing my pyjamas, I met a group of plainly hostile colleagues. I continued my visits for a few months, and things did improve, but I was never very popular!

From 1950 to 1952 I was subwarden of Merton College and on occasion had to stand in for the warden. I went to represent the college at a function in Folkestone where a wreath was laid at the statue of William Harvey (who was born there and was also a former warden of Merton). This was no particular occasion, but a project by the mayor to encourage the tourist trade. In aid of this, the ceremony was followed by a very grand luncheon. There I saw for the first and only time in my life a man so drunk that he seemed to get shorter and shorter and eventually slid down and completely disappeared under the table.

There are some general practitioners who do not mind if you turn up to a consultation in a sports jacket, others who think that you should be dressed like a consulting physician. In the 1950s one of the latter type (Dr Donald Olliff) asked me to see a patient, so I put on my best suit and gave my shoes an extra polish. The patient lived in a cottage which could be reached only by crossing a ploughed field. As it was pouring with rain, I arrived covered in mud looking more like a scarecrow than a physician. The patient was a man aged 103 whose sole topic of conversation was how these new railways had interfered with horse traffic. He had never got round to motor cars or aeroplanes.

Shortly afterwards I went to examine in Cambridge. My wife and I stayed with our old friends, the Leslie Coles*. Next day our housekeeper, Miss Price, telephoned to say that our daughter Jane had a stomach-ache. My wife at once said 'appendicitis.' I asked Miss Price a few questions which showed that the child had none of the classical symptoms, had not been sick, had no fever and had had a normal bowel action, so I made reassuring noises. My wife said: 'I am going home.' The child turned out to have a gangrenous appendix. Patients do not always play fair. My wife's comment was: 'Mothers' medical care is much more reliable than doctors' medical care.'

In 1954 the Association of Physicians met in Dublin. My wife and I stayed at the Shelbourne Hotel. On the day of our arrival there was a large luncheon party, attended by the President of Ireland, the ex-President, the Prime Minister of Ireland, the ex-Prime Minister and a lot of men wearing green sashes. It was a considerable lunch and went on till 6 in the evening. I asked what it was all about. It turned out that they had been unveiling a large block of granite in St Stephen's Green in memory of an Irishman who had been killed by the British in the 18th century. I have a child-like interest in facts, so I asked an Irish friend who this man was. He told me, but I had never heard of him before. 'Don't worry,' said my friend, 'neither have they.'

At the Association dinner we drank the health of the King of England and of the President of Ireland. For the latter toast all the doctors from Ulster remained seated, a remarkable display of bigotry and bad manners. The official record of the meeting, published in the *Quarterly Journal of Medicine,* records that on the last morning Dr A. M. Cooke asked a professor a powerful question about ammonia metabolism in the brain. Dr Cooke was in fact having breakfast in the hotel at the time. It is my favourite publication.

In July 1957 Charles Best* gave the Banting Memorial lecture in Oxford. He and his wife stayed with us, and I then learnt how he came to discover insulin. When Banting* was starting his research he required an assistant. The Dean of the medical school therefore nominated two very unwilling medical students, of whom Best was one. Neither wished to give up his summer vacation to work in a laboratory, so they decided that by the toss of a coin they would determine which should escape this unpleasant chore. Best lost.

On February 6th, 1960 Sir George Pickering*, Regius Professor of Medicine, for a change took his students for a ward round to the Horton General Hospital, Banbury. A foreign house physician gave a very poor history, ending with the words: 'In fact, the patient's only complaint is indigestion.' George, who had strong views on the precise use of the English language, said coldly: 'I do not know the meaning of the word "indigestion".' Whereupon the patient in the next bed said: 'Gawd, calls himself a specialist, too.'

About this time I gave a lecture at the Royal Army Medical College at Millbank. The best part was being called 'Sir' by a lieutenant-general.

My next-door neighbour was a distinguished scientist. His wife had a baby, and some months later I said to him, the way one does: 'How is the baby getting on?' His reply was: 'I am a little worried about him. He has doubled his birth weight in six months. If he goes on at this rate, by the time he is ten he will weigh over a million pounds, about 458 tons.'

A well known medical after-dinner speaker once had to propose the health of Lord Horder. He pointed out that Horder was there to look after you all through your life, in fact from the womb to the tomb. Before you were conceived he was president of the Eugenic Society. If you did not wish to be born he was president of the Birth Control Society. During your lifetime he was president of numerous societies working for your welfare and when you died he was president of the Cremation Society. He did not desert you even then. He was president of the Smoke Abatement Society.

The clinicopathological conference is one where a doctor who has never seen the patient is given all the data (except perhaps the one fact that reveals the diagnosis) about a problem patient, and has to discuss the facts and try to arrive at the diagnosis. This exercise was started at the Massachusetts General Hospital. After fifty years a book was published giving a number of the more interesting and puzzling cases shown over that period. I received the book for review. Progress in some parts of medicine had been so great that in some cases any of my students could have solved the problem at once. Others remained just as obscure. Even in gout, a disease that has been extensively studied since classical times, our knowledge of the cause has not changed since Aretaeus of Cappadocia wrote in the second century AD: 'The proximate cause of this disease is known only to the Gods.'

One Christmas the Radcliffe Infirmary Carol Club decided to visit the homes of four or five senior members of the medical staff. They came to my house first. My wife had provided such good refreshments that when they left at 1.30 in the morning there was no time to visit anybody else.

After one Christmas my wife felt very unwell, which she attributed to overindulgence in alcohol. She was so ill that I put her in a nursing home where she lay full of contrition. After a few days she developed jaundice, and was able to relax with a genuine disease. About three weeks later I took her to convalesce at a country hotel. We sat down to what looked like a good dinner but I could not eat it. I too became jaundiced thirty days after her although I had had almost no contact with her.

I never cease to marvel at the human body and how it deals with all the hazards of life. I once had a patient who every day for fifty years had given himself three or four injections of adrenalin for asthma. He never sterilized the syringe or needle, never applied any antiseptic at the injection site and sometimes made the injection through his trousers. There was never any skin sepsis. This also goes for diabetes, a condition prone to sepsis. Many diabetics have poor injection technique but skin infection is virtually unknown.

In about 1966 my wife complained of a pain in one breast. I examined it and found a lump about the size of a pea. Next day I took her to a surgeon, who at first could not find the lump. I went on at him till he did. Next day she had a mastectomy. Histology showed a malignant tumour, but no evidence of spread. Shortly after, she had some urinary symptoms. As she had had four large children it seemed that she might have some uterine prolapse. She was seen by a gynaecologist who found nothing amiss. He also did a cervical smear which was normal. A year later she received a postcard suggesting another cervical smear. 'I am not going,' she said. I said: 'You jolly well are.' The smear turned out to be very abnormal, so she had a hysterectomy. She died many years later from a condition totally unrelated to these two cancers. The moral of these events is: 'Do not delay but get on with it at once.'

When it became time for me to retire I had to go on for nearly two more years because of difficulties in appointing my two successors. When I did retire in March 1966 my wife said: 'The bad news is that I married you for better or worse, but not for lunch. The good news is that after thirty-five years I shall no longer have to give your secretaries coffee and have to hear all about their love life.' There were jollifications and my kind colleagues had my portrait done in pastels by Mr William Dring*, who specialized in the portraiture of children, so I have rather pink, smooth, chubby cheeks.

There were dinners, one in New College by about forty of my former registrars and house physicians. One ex-registrar, David Pyke, could not attend because he was in the United States, but he sent a telegram:- LAMENT ABSENCE WARMEST SALUTATIONS STOP CANNOT CABLE MORE AS IT COSTS MORE THAN YOU THINK DAVID PYKE. I was presented with a handsome book on architecture. The executive committee of the Association of Physicians and the editors of the *Quarterly Journal of Medicine* gave me a dinner and a silver salver engraved with the signatures of the six editors. An old family friend, a notable Mrs Maladroit, said: 'What a pity they scratched their names on that nice tray.' Retirement is surprisingly hard work and I came to think that it was really the job for a younger man.

In May 1987 I went to represent the Royal College of Physicians at the tercentenary celebrations of the death of Sir William Petty* at Romsey, in Hampshire, where he was born and is buried. Although a physician, he is better known as an extraordinary polymath – a linguist, served in the Royal Navy, later became physician to the Army in Ireland, a Fellow of

...so I have rather pink, smooth, chubby cheeks

the Royal Society, professor of anatomy at Oxford, professor of music at Gresham College, London, and a Member of Parliament. He wrote on population, taxation, customs duties, lotteries, trade and banking. With John Graunt he wrote the first book ever on vital statistics. He surveyed Ireland, invented a double-hulled ship, the catamaran, a wheel to ride on, precursor of the bicycle, and when challenged to a duel chose as his weapon a dark cellar and a large axe.

In the view of many people, the constant references to sex in the press and on television introduce children too early and too often to the facts of life. This has not always been so. My parents were great friends of a schoolmaster and his wife, both aged about fifty. He had a first class degree from Cambridge and they were among the most intelligent and cultivated people that I have ever met. When I was a medical student I spent a weekend at their country cottage. During a walk my host asked me if babies were born through the umbilicus. I thought at first that this was a silly, if not tasteless joke, but it turned out that he was totally unaware of the facts of life.

The many changes in medicine over the years need no stressing, but there have been equally numerous changes in nursing. It is not many years since nurses did housework and scrubbed the floors. It was unthinkable that they should do anything as technical as taking the blood pressure. Now, rightly, they do all kinds of technical jobs. As a result they are apt to regard themselves as equals in the medical team. There is no harm in this, but somebody must be in charge to take responsibility for vital decisions. If nurses have a fault, it is that, like junior house officers, they are tending to develop a 9 to 5 mentality. One of my very senior medical colleagues used to maintain that nursing had sadly deteriorated. In the good old days, he said, if you went into a ward bathroom there was always a probationer sobbing behind the door.

CHAPTER SEVENTEEN

Specialization

I have often been asked what my specialty was. When I was appointed to the Radcliffe Infirmary in 1932 there was no specialization. I was a cardiologist, chest physician, gastroenterologist, neurologist, hepatologist, nephrologist, haematologist and paediatrician. There was just one subject – Medicine. Later I did develop some special interests. The first was in accurate diagnosis, on the grounds that unless you have a firm diagnosis you cannot treat the patient rationally. Not knowing the treatment is unimportant – you can always ask somebody or look it up in a book.

During the war there was a large influx of patients to Oxford from London, including of course a number of diabetics. Robin Lawrence*, of the King's College Hospital clinic, wrote complaining that there was no clinic in Oxford for his patients; so, in 1940 I started the diabetic clinic at the Radcliffe Infirmary and naturally became very interested in this disease.

One of my many failings is that I take up a special interest or hobby with enthusiasm, but if another one appears interesting I abandon the former. In 1953 I was invited to give the Lumleian Lectures at the Royal College of Physicians of London. While wondering what on earth to talk about I saw a patient with gross osteoporosis, immediately became fascinated by this disease and gave the lectures on it.

I next became interested in the epidemiology of fractures, which then had been little studied. An eminent retired doctor asked the Ministry of Health if it was true that fractures in the elderly were becoming more frequent. A committee was formed, of which I was a member. A preliminary survey showed that that was certainly so in the case of fractured neck of femur. I used to criticize the orthopaedic surgeons for worrying more about how many fins the pin should have that was used for fixing the neck of the fractured femur, than about how the patient came to sustain the fracture in the first place.

A young orthopaedic surgeon, A. J. Buhr, and I studied over 8,500 fractures and showed that fractures of different sites fell into well-defined patterns related to age, sex and occupation. One observation was that fractured neck of femur in men over 80 is 30 times commoner than in young men, and that in women over 80 the same ratio is 300 times. The paper, entitled 'Fracture patterns' appeared in *The Lancet* in March 1959 and was well received. In fact, I was asked to give some lectures about it in the United States. The references at the end include a pleasant juxtaposition:

Cicero, M. T. (BC 44) *De Senectute*
Cooke, A. M. (1955) *Lancet,* i, 877, 929

I did not tell anybody, but thought to myself that this time we had got something right, chiefly because we had used a new method of enquiry. Pride goeth before a fall. I then discovered that all this work had been done in 1821 by Sir Astley Cooper* at Guy's Hospital. He wrote a large book on fractures and dislocations. No modern orthopaedic surgeon could teach him anything clinical. Without X-rays he had to decide whether it was a fracture or a dislocation. Incidentally, in those civilized days his house surgeons all wore tail coats.

Cooper also wrote a smaller book on fractured neck of femur. He knew about intra-capsular and extra-capsular fractures, and made injection specimens to show the blood supply of the area. This was an eye opener. I did have the decency to visit St Paul's Cathedral and bow before his tomb. I have since maintained an interest in the skeleton, partly because when the specialists have removed all their special organs and tissues there is nothing else left, and more importantly because it is of great metabolic interest.

With the increasing complexity and technology of medicine, specialization is inevitable, but it can be, and sometimes is, carried to absurd lengths.

One cardiologist to another: 'Have you any special interest?'

'Yes, heart block.'

'Really, partial or complete?'

I accept the general thesis that the idea is to get the patient right by any means available. One of my pupils went into paediatrics and specialized in the lungs. Before long he found himself confined to one lung and later to one segment of that lung. He saw the light and transferred to a wider branch.

Another aspect of specialization is related to secessions from the old Royal Colleges. The Royal College of Physicians of London, founded in 1518, and the Royal College of Surgeons of England, founded in 1745 as the Company of Surgeons, between them used to embrace all branches of the medical arts except general practice. The foundation of the Royal College of General Practitioners in 1972 filled this gap.

In 1937 the first branch of medicine to break away from the old Colleges was the Royal College of Obstetricians and Gynaecologists. Other branches followed – the Royal College of Pathologists in 1964, the Royal College of Psychiatrists in 1971 and the Royal College of Anaesthetists in 1992. In 1993, an attempt was being made by the paediatricians to secede. I am strongly opposed to this and was moved to write a somewhat intemperate letter to the *Journal of the Royal College of Physicians,* as follows.

22.7.93.
Dear Editor,
I write to protest against the proposed formation of a Royal College of Paediatricians. It is quite unnecessary. Paediatrics is an important branch of medicine, but so are cardiology, chest medicine, gastroenterology, neurology, nephrology, hepatology, haematology, endocrinology, dermatology, etc. All branches are equally important to the general body of medicine. Each new college diminishes the prestige and power of the existing colleges. When is it going to stop? If the present trend continues, the next thing will be a college for every disease. I look forward, sadly, to Royal Colleges of Flat Feet and Halitosis.

Yours sincerely
A. M. COOKE

The extent of specialization is also shown by the special interests of the editors of a journal devoted to medicine (in its narrowest sense). These are given as:

Genetics and Immunology	Molecular Haematology
Infection and Molecular Biology	Dermatology
Clinical Pharmacology	Neurology
Metabolic Medicine	Gastroenterology
Oncology	Molecular Genetics
Cardiology	Endocrinology
Epidemiology	Hepatology
Lungs	Rheumatology
Nephrology	Infection and Tropical Medicine
Neurogenetics	Diabetes
Clinical Genetics	

Ever-increasing specialization has almost abolished the general physician. There is still room for someone who can look at the patient as a whole. I have noticed that when ultra-specialists are ill, they always avoid their own kind and seek the advice of a generalist.

Another result of progress and specialization is the decline of purely clinical medicine, due largely to the modern passion for investigations. I have heard a physician rebuke his house physician for not doing enough investigations. If I rebuked mine it would be for doing too many. Investigations cost money, take other people's time, may carry hazards, may be very unpleasant for the patient and may be useless. I once had under my care a patient with florid scurvy. The house physician and registrar at once proposed estimation of vitamin C in the plasma. I forbade it on the grounds that it would be a waste of the taxpayers' money to try to estimate something that you knew was not there. If there had been a trace of the vitamin in the plasma the patient would not have had frank scurvy.

The retention of knowledge of purely clinical medicine is of crucial importance. In war, a hurricane, an explosion, an underground accident, an aeroplane crash on a mountain, earthquake, volcanic eruption, tidal wave or in the middle of a desert there are likely to be no accessory aids, but doctors will still be expected to diagnose and treat their patients.

I think that an experienced physician who went round an ordinary medical ward and took proper histories would know the diagnosis in at least two out of three cases without physical examination.

One of the charms of medicine is its variety. There is no part of the body without interest. If you decided to investigate such unpromising areas as the pinna or the perirenal fat or the big toe, you would probably find them full of interest, and there would be a surprisingly large literature on the subject.

Medical education

It has been said on many occasions that present-day medical students are not as good as they used to be. I disagree. I find present-day students intelligent, hardworking, highly motivated and humane. They have to learn additional subjects that did not exist in my day. As a matter of history, a few subjects have been removed from the curriculum. One is pharmacognosy, if anyone still knows what that is; it is now taught only in a tiny department at the School of Pharmacy. Before there were tablets or capsules, pills had to be made up from the raw drugs, and every doctor had to know opium, orris root, senna, digitalis leaves or rhubarb when he saw them. I have passed an examination in this subject, not from knowledge but by inspired guessing.

It is plain that students cannot learn all branches of medicine, but it is good that they should be exposed, however briefly, to all of them, for two reasons. One is so that they will not be floored by a simple question from a layman, and the other so that they will know what careers are open to them.

There is an art in teaching, and enthusiasm is a very important factor. The late Sir Hugh Cairns, although he worked in the highly specialized field of neurosurgery, was an excellent teacher of general medical principles. Postgraduate education, to which there is no end, can best be carried out by doing a variety of jobs.

The students at the Oxford hospitals were a lively lot and, as at St Thomas's, had ribald pantomimes in which they pilloried their teachers. Some productions had good titles – *The Lady with the Lump, Handsome and Dettol, Snow White or CO_2 and the Seven Warts, Careless Rupture, Kind Hearts and Coronaries*. I was impersonated as *Sir Baldasa Coot,* and always carried a bunch of sweet peas, blue, green, yellow and orange, the colours of Fehling's solution. My impersonator, Derrick Bolsover, had me absolutely to the life. The next year it was decided that I should appear in person. Derrick and I had our make-up done together. He was fitted with a bald wig, which was covered with greasepaint to make it as shiny as my scalp. If I was too shiny, some powder was applied to my scalp. When I appeared the audience gasped and some thought that I had gone mad or had come on to protest. Derrick and I had a brief conversation, including: 'Didn't I see you when shaving this morning?' This was during the war, and when we walked about the darkened hospital the nurses never knew whether it was a physician or a medical student. When we visited the pub across the road, some of the more seasoned topers thought that they were seeing double.

CHAPTER EIGHTEEN

Progress

Looking back over 75 years, it is tempting to examine medical progress. Some years ago in Denmark the professors of medicine were asked to write down what they thought would be the directions of research and progress in the following ten years. The answers were locked in a safe until the ten years had elapsed. One professor thought that there might be something about chromosomes; the others were all wildly wrong.

Medicine is never static. Its progress is a large subject, and in a little book like this can be treated only superficially. There are new methods of investigation and diagnosis, new diseases such as the acquired immune deficiency syndrome (AIDS), new apparatus, new operations, new drugs and indeed new branches of medicine and surgery, such as geriatrics, intensive care and aerospace medicine.

There are new concepts, and there are old ideas, cherished beliefs, to be discarded. A drug in common use may be found to be ineffective or even dangerous. The attitudes of doctors to patients and of patients to doctors change. Nursing shares in these new developments. Medical education is under constant review.

There has been much legislation relating to medicine, drugs and public health. It is possible to mention only the more important Acts such as:

The Pharmacy and Poisons Act, 1933, the Midwives Act, 1936, the Medical Act, 1936, the Disabled Persons (Employment) Act, 1944, the National Health Service Act, 1948 (see Chapter 10), the Hypnosis Act, 1952, the Clean Air Acts, 1956-1968, the Therapeutic Substances Act, 1956, the Dentists Act, 1957, the Human Tissues Act, 1961, the Abortion Act, 1961, the Criminal Procedure (Insanity) Act, 1964, the Abortion Act, 1967, the Medicines Act, 1968, the Employer's Liability (Defective Equipment) Act, 1969, the paternalistic Tattooing of Minors Act, 1969, the Chronically Sick and Disabled Persons Act, 1970, the Food and Drugs (Milk) Act, 1970, the Misuse of Drugs Act, 1971, the Social Security Acts, 1973, 1975, the Adoption Act, 1976, the Mental Health Act, 1983 and the last Medical Act, 1983, the Data Protection Act, 1984, the Access to Health Records Act, 1991, the Still-Birth (Definition) Act, 1992.

Methods of diagnosis. Whatever changes have taken place, history-taking and clinical examination remain the cheapest and extremely effective method of diagnosis. X-rays, discovered in 1895, were first used to detect fractures and metallic foreign bodies. In 1921 began the introduction of lipiodol and other radio-opaque material into the urinary tract, the gastrointestinal tract, the vascular system, including the brain and the coronary arteries, the gall bladder, the cerebrospinal fluid and the lungs. Image intensifiers, phase contrast microscopy, electron microscopy, cineradiography and computerized axial tomography (in 1973) followed. In gastroenterology, flexible fibreoptic endoscopy has proved a valuable tool. The brain scan provides a series of optical sections of the brain.

When I started medicine my chief instrument was a five shilling stethoscope. Two of the new methods of investigation now cost hundreds of thousands of pounds; one is ultrasound, derived from the sonar used for military purposes in World War II and brought into clinical use in the 1950s. In 1988 I was examined by ultrasound and the results were displayed on a television screen. I was given a conducted tour of my own abdomen – 'there is your right kidney, that is your gallbladder, there is your left kidney and here is your spleen'. This method is painless and harmless, but expensive.

The other is nuclear magnetic resonance (also painless, harmless and expensive); at first a tool of the physicist, it was applied to medicine at the end of the 1960s and provides pictures of great clarity.

Biochemistry or clinical chemistry can now identify and measure immense numbers of blood and tissue constituents, blood gases, enzymes, drug levels and hormone levels. New methods of investigation include the photoelectric colorimeter, radioimmunoassay and measurement of pH. Some landmarks were the discovery of the source of urea in 1932, the discovery of adenosine triphosphate in 1929, discovery of the order of sequence of the amino acids in insulin, and the advent of genetic engineering in 1975. The computer and the word processor are now essential tools.

Anaesthetics. Gone are the days of open ether and open chloroform. I had open ether in 1922 and took three days to recover. The modern intravenous anaesthetic leaves no hangover. I had one in 1988 for a prostate operation at 9 am, lasting for about an hour. I woke up at about 10.30 and, to the slight disapproval of the nursing staff, ate a large lunch at 12.00. Spinal anaesthesia came in about 1940.

Medical therapy. Hundreds of new drugs have been developed, many being variants of old drugs such as aperients, sedatives, analgesics, anticoagulants, drugs to lower the blood pressure and drugs to alter the mood. In 1924 came BCG vaccine against tuberculosis, and other antibacterial sera (notably for pneumonia), but the antibacterial sera were largely replaced by chemotherapy and antibiotics – sulphanilamide (1935) and its successors, penicillin (1940) and streptomycin (1944). Other important drugs are cortisone (1949) and interferon (1957).

On the non-drug side came the iron lung in 1928, intensive care units in 1941, the artificial kidney in 1943 and hospices for the dying in 1948.

Physiotherapy and occupational therapy have expanded, in particular with devices to help the disabled. In preventive medicine, poliomyelitis and tuberculosis have almost been abolished in this country. The major event, it is worth repeating, was the elimination of smallpox from the world in 1980, and there are improved preventive vaccines.

Cardiology. Cardiac catheterization in 1929 and new electrocardiographic leads were followed mainly by surgical advances – enlarging mitral stenosis (1923), defibrillator (1947), external pacemaker (1952), implanted pacemaker (1960), operations for persistent ductus arteriosus and for coarctation of the aorta, new plastic heart valves (1961), new pig heart valves (1968), the heart-lung pump and in 1967 the first successful cardiac transplant. Replacement of obstructed coronary arteries with systemic veins is a notable advance. Another less spectacular but important advance in 1950 was external cardiac resuscitation as a first-aid technique.

Respiratory medicine. In the respiratory system, advances were the discovery in the 1950s that smoking causes lung cancer and other troubles, and the control of infections with antibiotics.

Nutrition. This fashionable subject has been so much in the news that every woman's magazine advocates a different diet. My wife pointed out one basic principle – 'Anything you like is bad for you.'

Paediatrics. The major advances have been the control of infections by antibiotics, the care of premature infants, the diagnosis of Down's syndrome by cytology, the early intrauterine diagnosis of malformations by ultrasound, and even how many cusps a heart valve has. Cot deaths remain a problem.

Molecular medicine. From 1940, studies of sickle-cell anaemia and thalassaemia have led to the disentanglement of the structure of the various kinds of human haemoglobin, normal and abnormal. The unfolding of the structure of DNA in 1953 caused the application of scientific genetics to clinical medicine and the development of an important new branch of medicine – molecular medicine. With restriction enzymes it is now possible to pick out individual genes, join them up and insert them into different places, or even in different animals. Gene libraries are being built up. As well as its scientific interest, molecular medicine offers practical help in various genetic disorders. Genetic fingerprinting is a valuable advance. Molecular medicine is also making an impact on oncology, the study of tumours, mostly malignant.

Neurology. A current interest is senile dementia, often wrongly called Alzheimer's disease. Advancing years tend to damage the mind so that people over 80 often lose their memory, especially for recent events, and other mental functions. This condition is senile dementia. In 1907 the German neurologist Alois Alzheimer described a condition indistinguishable from senile dementia but occurring in patients aged 40. That is Alzheimer's disease. The term senile dementia suggests decay and improbable recovery, so all the public and many doctors prefer the term Alzheimer's disease, which suggests not decay but a disease which one might contract and which might be curable.

Surgery. As well as improvements in technique there have been organ transplants. The earliest was the kidney (1954). One of the first carried out in Britain was about 1960 when Dr Edwin Clark, a general practitioner in Reading, received a kidney from his partner. Unhappily he died because at that time little was known about the problems of rejection. Later, while waiting for the operation, patients were kept alive by a dialysis machine or by peritoneal dialysis.

Other transplants were heart, first performed in 1967, lung and liver. Replacement of joints such as the hip joint (1960), knee joints and even finger joints has become common. Transurethral prostatectomy was an important advance.

In Ear, Nose and Throat surgery the treatment of deafness has been advanced by operative microscopy, that of nasal disease by endoscopes. The treatment of laryngeal disease has been aided by improved endoscopes and the carbon dioxide laser, and by vocal prostheses for patients who have undergone laryngectomy.

A recent advance has been 'keyhole surgery' where gallstones or even organs are removed piecemeal through a small incision in the abdominal wall. This results in no more three-week convalescence after surgery, surrounded by grapes and magazines: now you may well be home in 48 hours and back to the office or the kitchen sink.

World War II greatly advanced plastic surgery. I developed ectropion (where the lower eyelid sags forward). The plastic surgeons jacked up the eyelids by grafting below them small strips of skin taken from behind my ears.

An extension of plastic surgery is aesthetic surgery, devoted to reshaping breasts and bottoms; it is thought by the orthodox not to be respectable. Indeed, the insertion of plastic implants in the breast has proved to be disastrous.

The surgery of the eye has developed – corneal grafting, repair of detached retina, muscle advancement for squint, acrylic lenses and operations for glaucoma.

Orthopaedic surgery has improved accident surgery and the treatment of malformations.

Obstetrics. Chemotherapy and better management have reduced the maternal death rate in normal childbirth from 1 in 100 to less than 1 in 10,000 (Irvine Loudon). The oral contraceptive was introduced in 1956, and the first test tube baby, Louise Brown, was born in Oldham, Lancashire, in 1978.

Fringe medicine. Not exactly an advance, but a change has been the ever-increasing public interest in fringe or alternative medicine, largely fostered by the media and by the propaganda of its practitioners (see Chapter 14). My view is that patients are treated by the practitioners they deserve.

Advances come and go. The influence of diet and other environmental factors on heart disease and on health in general seems to vary from week to week.

I conclude by describing a ward round at an Oxford hospital 25 years hence. The party consists of a physician, one senior registrar, two middle registrars, three junior registrars, four house physicians, the ward sister, a secretary, assorted therapists and social workers, and one medical student. There is no room for any more.

The physician says: 'Now, what have we got today?'

A house physician says: 'A patient with a pain in the knee.'

'What is the history?' asks the physician.

The house physician looks blank. One of the registrars comes to his rescue and says: 'History-taking was abolished by a Ministry of Health directive five years ago.'

The physician then says 'What about the physical examination?' Again the house physician looks blank.

The registrar says: 'That too has been abolished.'

'Of course,' says the physician, 'it is sometimes difficult for us senior men to keep up with all the latest advances in medicine. Have you done any investigations?'

The house physician says: 'Of course; X rays, ultrasound, biochemical profile, all hormone levels, NMR and the rest'

'What did they show?'

'Nothing at all'

'What did you do next?'

'We got in the new Totalometer, which showed that the 54th gene on the 8th chromosome was 2.357 kilocycles out of phase.'

'But which type of kilocycle?'

'Sorry; I should have said – C5, type Beta.'

'Well done, my boy. Treatment?'

'The patient is doing well on aspirin.'

As they move on to the next bed the physician says to a registrar: 'Smith, would you ask the computing department to let us have the print-out up to the ward sooner? I *would* like to have known the patient's age and sex.'

Epilogue

Looking back over 75 years of medicine, what do I think about it all? The first thing is that I have had more than my fair share of good luck. I was born into a solid professional family whose members have followed occupations such as doctor, parson, architect, journalist, engineer, head master, bank manager, soldier, company secretary, and the like. My parents believed in education, not only at school but in the outer world. As we lived in London I was taken to the British Museum, the Natural History Museum, the Science Museum, other lesser museums, the Zoological Gardens, the Royal Geographical Society, the Royal Society of Arts, Gresham College, Madame Tussaud's, Kew Gardens, Hampton Court, the Tower of London, the London Docks, to see Blériot's aeroplane in which he flew the Channel in 1909, to see Halley's comet in 1910, to see the funeral of Edward VII in the same year and to see the first cinema, the Bioscope, in Regent Street.

My family has gone in for longevity. My great-uncle Edward reached 97, my father 92, his brother Willie 95, his brother Frank 102, my sister Dorothy 100. Guy Silk and Muriel Silk, children of my father's sister, Margaret, reached 92 and 94 and a cousin, Geoffrey Cooke, a son of my father's brother, Dr Cecil Cooke, is 91 and I am 95 – a total of nine nonagenarians, or older.

My school days are described in the Prologue. My next pieces of good luck were not to be killed in World War I, to get into Oxford, to choose medicine as a career and to marry the right girl. It is often said that marriage is a gamble, and this is certainly true. A young man goes to a dance and meets a good-looking girl with an attractive figure. They become friendly, later become engaged and eventually marry. Neither has the faintest idea of how the marriage will turn out or what it will be like in 20 or 30 years time.

Our marriage turned out to be a success. It started as a gamble because I met Vera at a fancy dress dance where we were both heavily disguised. We had 56 years of great happiness together. Here is a small piece of advice to those entering matrimony: you cannot possibly agree on all matters all the time, so the first thing to learn is how to differ without

...and I am 95

quarrelling.

A special piece of good fortune was to choose medicine as a career. I could not have wished for a more interesting or satisfying occupation. I have never had two days alike and I have never had an uninteresting day. Of course there are bad moments, and nobody can fail to be moved by pain, suffering, death and bereavement. On the other hand there are many good moments. I have much preferred working in Oxford to working in London where you cannot become a Fellow of one of the better Oxford Colleges. I was also fortunate in having good health and in not being a worrier. Lastly, none of my 17 descendants has taken to drink, drugs, or crime. In the modern world that is certainly good luck. I may add that my children have inherited some of the low cunning of their father. When my son, John, did his DPhil, he chose such an obscure topic that the authorities had to ask him if he could suggest some suitable examiners.

My wife and I gained great pleasure from foreign travel. I have been to Spain, Portugal, France, Belgium, the Netherlands, Germany, Norway,

Sweden, Denmark, Czechoslovakia, Russia, Austria, Hungary, Switzerland, Italy, Malta, Greece, Turkey, Egypt, India, the United States, Mexico, Canada, Romania and Ukraine.

In my life I have had four extraordinary escapes from death. (1) In 1918 I was in a stationary aeroplane that caught fire; I managed to get out in time. (2) Vera and I were once walking on a mountain in Switzerland in the spring and came across what looked like a patch of snow. I walked on to it, but it was ice. I fell over and began to slide down a slope at increasing speed to what we later found was a precipice. I caught my foot on the only piece of rock in sight. (3) I was motoring to London on a Sunday afternoon. While going at 60 mph I suddenly fell asleep. The car swerved, fortunately not into the oncoming traffic, but to the near side up a grassy bank. I was woken by a rough ride and an inclination of about 30°; also, the car missed all the traffic signs and other obstacles. It was the only safe place for miles around. The reason was a very cold day and a very hot car heater. (4) Vera and I were motoring along a straight road when a car coming towards us suddenly skidded on an icy patch and shot across our bows into the nearside hedge. Our combined speeds must have been over 100 mph and the two cars missed each other by less than a foot.

Most of us have some secret ambition. Mine is to found a society whose function will be to make two annual pilgrimages: the first, to desecrate the grave of the man who invented the internal combustion engine, which is responsible for both the motor-car and aerial warfare, the second to desecrate the grave of the man who invented the telephone. I expect large numbers to join.

Many and revolutionary changes have occurred in medicine in the 75 years since I was a medical student, and doubtless this process will continue. On the other hand, the basic principles remain exactly the same. Take a proper history and do not forget to ask if the patient has been abroad and if so where to; make a full clinical examination, do only really necessary investigations; and then THINK.

Biographical details of individuals mentioned in the text

Christopher Addison, later Viscount Addison, KG, FRCP, FRCS (1869–1951), was a professor of anatomy at Sheffield from 1897 to 1901, and then lectured in anatomy at Charing Cross Hospital, London. He entered Parliament as a Liberal MP in 1910 and was Minister of Munitions during World War I, then Minister of Reconstruction. In 1918 he became the first Minister of Health.

Sir Frederick Banting, KBE, FRCP, FRS (1891–1941), was a Canadian physician who with Charles Best and JJR Macleod discovered insulin in 1922. He and Macleod shared the 1923 Nobel Prize for medicine.

Charles Best, CBE, FRCP, FRS (1899–1978), was a student when with Frederick Banting he discovered insulin. He later became professor of physiology at Toronto.

Sir William Beveridge, later Lord Beveridge (1879–1963), a barrister, economist, social reformer and Master of University College, Oxford, is best remembered for the *Report on Social Insurance and Allied Services* (1942) – the 'Beveridge Report' – which was the foundation of the welfare state.

James Birley, CBE, FRCP (1884–1934), was a neurologist to St Thomas's Hospital.

Blackwell's is a leading Oxford bookshop.

Charles Box, FRCP (1866–1951), became the senior physician to St Thomas's Hospital. He had special interests in fevers and morbid anatomy. I was his house physician.

Russell Brain, later Lord Brain, FRCP, FRS (1895–1967), was a distinguished neurologist on the staffs of the Maida Vale and London hospitals. He was President of the Royal College of Physicians of London from 1950 to 1957. He was a philosopher, poet and literary critic, and an honorary member of many societies and committees.

Isambard Kingdom Brunel (1806–1859) was an engineer and inventor. He helped his father, Sir Marc Isambard Brunel, to construct the Thames Tunnel. He built three pioneer steamships, including the *Great Britain*, now preserved at Bristol where she was launched.

Sir Farquhar Buzzard, Bart, KCVO, FRCP (1871–1945), was physician to King George V, and neurologist to St Thomas's Hospital. In 1928 he moved to Oxford as Regius Professor of Medicine. He played a large part in Lord Nuffield's medical benefaction and in founding the modern Oxford Clinical Medical School.

E. M. (Teddy) Buzzard, FRCP, (1909–1976), was Sir Farquhar's son and a physician in Oxford.

Sir Hugh Cairns, KBE, FRCS (1896–1952), was an Australian Rhodes Scholar at Oxford who became a distinguished neurosurgeon and held the position of Nuffield Professor of Surgery at Oxford. He played a significant role in obtaining Lord Nuffield's medical benefaction and in the foundation of the modern Oxford Clinical Medical School.

Sir Maurice Cassidy, GCVO, CB, FRCP (1880–1949), was a physician to St Thomas's Hospital and to King George VI. He was also chief medical officer to the Metropolitan Police.

Neville Chamberlain (1869–1940) was a Conservative statesman who became Minister of Health twice in the 1920s, and again briefly in 1931. As Prime Minister 1937–1940 he tried in vain to avert World War II.

William Cheselden, FRS (1688–1752), was a leading anatomist and surgeon to St Thomas's, St George's and Chelsea hospitals.

Sir Walter Chiesman, CB, FRCP (1900–1973), was an authority on industrial medicine. He became medical adviser to the Treasury.

Sir Winston Churchill, KG, OM, CH, FRS (1874–1965), after an adventurous military and political career became Prime Minister (1940–1945) during World War II, which he played a large part in winning for Britain. Before World War I he introduced a Bill to insure against unemployment. A notable orator and writer, he was awarded the 1953 Nobel Prize for literature.

Sir George Clark (1890–1979) was a distinguished historian who was successively Fellow of All Souls and Fellow of Oriel, Oxford, where he became Chichele Professor of Economic History. He was later professor of modern history at Cambridge and Fellow of Trinity. He returned to Oxford as Provost of Oriel. He held many academic honours.

Henry Cohen, later Lord Cohen of Birkenhead, CB, FRCP (1900–1977), was a remarkable physician who received a consultant post less than two years after qualifying in medicine. He became professor of medicine at Liverpool. Later he was President of the British Medical Association, of the Royal Society of Medicine and of the General Medical Council. He was also an author, an administrator and an adviser to government departments.

Leslie Cole, FRCP (1898–1983), was a leading physician in Cambridge and Dean of the postgraduate medical school there. He was also an authority on tetanus, a rare disease but relatively common in East Anglia.

William Collier, FRCP (1889–1932), was a gifted and much loved Oxford physician and pathologist whose early death led to my replacing him at the Radcliffe Infirmary.

HRH the Duke of Connaught, Prince Arthur William Patrick Albert (1850–1942), was the seventh child and third son of Queen Victoria.

Miss Ina Cook was for many years Secretary of the Royal College of Physicians of London.

Sir Astley Cooper, FRCS (1768–1841), was a leading surgeon of his day at Guy's Hospital.

Harvey Cushing (1869–1939) was an American surgeon who was the leading, and probably the first, exponent of neurosurgery. He became professor of surgery at Harvard in 1911.

Bertrand Dawson, later Viscount Dawson of Penn, GCVO, KCB, KCMG, FRCP (1864–1945), was a noted physician and man of affairs. He was physician to the London Hospital, and physician to King Edward VII, King George V, King Edward VIII, King George VI and Queen Mary. He had to do with the formation of the Ministry of Health in 1918 and in the same year proposed the creation of a comprehensive national health service. He was President of the Royal Society of Medicine, President of the British Medical Association, and from 1931 to 1938 President of the Royal College of Physicians of London. He was also a modest, humane and charming man.

Claude Douglas, CMG, FRS (1882–1963), was a noted respiratory physiologist and a Fellow of St John's College, Oxford. He invented the Douglas bag, used for collecting gas samples in respiratory physiology, and was my tutor.

William Dring, RA, a contemporary artist, gained fame as a portrait painter, especially of children. He also painted landscapes.

Leonard Dudgeon, CMG, CBE, FRCP (1876–1938), was professor of pathology and Dean of the Medical School at St Thomas's Hospital.

John (Jack) Elkington, FRCP (1904–1963), was neurologist to St Thomas's Hospital and the National Hospital for Nervous Diseases, Queen Square, London.

Leonard Findlay, FRCP (1878–1947), was a Scottish paediatrician who became professor of child health at Glasgow. For a time he was Director of the League of Nations Red Cross Society in Geneva. He was especially interested in rickets. In 1930 he moved to London, and during World War II to Oxford.

Charles Fletcher, CBE, FRCP, was formerly professor of clinical epidemiology at London University.

Abraham Flexner (1866–1959) was an American medical administrator and author who served as Secretary of the Rockefeller Foundation.

Howard Florey, later Lord Florey, FRCP, FRS (1898–1968), was born in Australia, but came from an Oxfordshire family. A Rhodes Scholarship brought him to Magdalen College, Oxford. He became professor of pathology at Sheffield and later at Oxford. The mould *Penicillium* had been shown to have antibacterial properties by Sir Alexander Fleming, but it was Florey who successfully applied it to medicine. He shared the 1945 Nobel Prize in medicine with Fleming and Ernst (later Sir Ernst) Chain. Florey was President of the Royal Society from 1960 to 1965 and later became Provost of the Queen's College, Oxford.

Sir Archibald Garrod, KCMG, FRCP, FRS (1857–1936), was professor of medicine at St Bartholomew's Hospital and physician to the Hospital for Sick Children, London. In 1909 he wrote a book, *Inborn Errors of Metabolism*, about chemical malformations, which opened an entirely new chapter in medicine. In 1920 he succeeded Sir William Osler as Regius Professor of Medicine at Oxford.

George Gask, FRCS (1875–1951), was professor of surgery at St Bartholomew's Hospital.

Alexander Gibson, FRCP (1875–1950), was a physician and pathologist to the Radcliffe Infirmary, Oxford. In 1937 he became Nuffield Reader in Pathology and a Fellow of Merton College, the first medical man to be so elected since 1860.

Sir William Goodenough, Bart (1899–1951), was a banker. He served as chairman of the Radcliffe Infirmary and of the Nuffield Trusts for developing the Oxford Medical School and founding Nuffield College.

Christian Friedrich Samuel Hahnemann (1755–1843) was a German physician who founded homoeopathy. When apothecaries refused to provide his minute doses of medicine he made them up himself and gave them to his patients, and was prosecuted in many German cities.

John (Jock) Burdon Sanderson Haldane, FRS (1892–1964), was the son of John Scott Haldane. After many years as professor of genetics and then of biometry at University College, London, he moved to India and became an Indian citizen.

John Scott Haldane, FRS (1860–1936), was a leading physiologist of his day. He was an expert on gases and their effect on the lungs and heart.

Richard Burdon Haldane, later Viscount Haldane, FRS (1856–1928), was an eminent judge and statesman who became Lord Chancellor three times. He served on several Royal Commissions and took an active interest in university administration. He was the brother of John Scott Haldane.

Emma Hamilton (c 1765–1815) was born Emily Lyon in Cheshire, and after a chequered career married the diplomat Sir William Hamilton in 1791. She became the mistress of the naval hero Lord Nelson.

William Harvey, FRCP (1578–1657), discovered the circulation of the blood – a landmark in medical history. He was physician to St Bartholomew's Hospital and for a short time Warden of Merton College, Oxford.

Frederick Hobson, DSO, FRCP (1891–1948), was a man of immense energy. In 1914 he joined the army as a dispatch rider and by 1917 was a brigade major. He started his medical career in Oxford in general practice, but later became a physician to the Radcliffe Infirmary. In 1936 he was Secretary of the British Medical Association Annual Meeting in Oxford.

Thomas Horder, later Lord Horder, GCVO, FRCP (1871–1955), was physician to St Bartholomew's Hospital, physician to King George VI and extra physician to Queen Elizabeth II. He was generally regarded as the best clinician of his day. He could be quarrelsome and perhaps for that reason failed to become President of the Royal College of Physicians of London.

Donald Hunter, CBE, FRCP (1898–1978), was a physician to the London Hospital and an authority on industrial medicine.

John Hunter, FRS (1728–1793), was a surgeon to St George's Hospital and later Surgeon-General to the army. He was a noted anatomist, zoologist and experimentalist, and the first surgeon to try to put surgery on a scientific basis.

Sir Arthur Hurst, FRCP (1879–1944), trained at Oxford and Guy's Hospital, where he was later a physician. During World War I he served in Salonika. He was later put in charge of a military hospital in Britain where he did notable work on war neuroses. Between the wars he ran a private medical clinic at Windsor. During World War II the clinic was closed and he came to Oxford to help with teaching. He won many medals and other awards.

Reginald Jewesbury, FRCP (1878–1971), took up paediatrics, then hardly a specialty, first at Charing Cross Hospital and later at St Thomas's. He was one of the founders of the British Paediatric Association and wrote a book, *Mothercraft, Prenatal and Postnatal.*

Sir Arbuthnot Lane, Bart, FRCS (1856–1943), was an eminent, but eccentric, surgeon. He founded the New Health Society in 1925.

Robin Lawrence, FRCP (1892–1968), an Aberdonian, started his medical career as a biochemist at King's College Hospital. He developed diabetes, for which there was then no treatment. As his prospects were bleak and he wished to spare his family and friends the pain of seeing him die, he went into general practice in Florence. He became steadily worse, but in 1923 was told about insulin. So he drove himself across Europe and arrived at King's College Hospital *in extremis*. He was saved by insulin. He was later appointed physician to the hospital and founded the first diabetic clinic in London, if not in the world. He also founded the British Diabetic Association and wrote extensively on the subject.

Sir Thomas Lewis, CBE, FRCP, FRS (1881–1945), was a physician to University College Hospital. He discovered auricular fibrillation, and did much to further the scientific study of medicine at the bedside.

Joseph Lister, later Lord Lister, FRCS, FRS (1827–1912), was professor of surgery at Glasgow, then Edinburgh and finally at King's College Hospital, London. Before his day, surgeons operated wearing old frock coats stained with blood and pus. The sepsis rate was enormous: in fact it was very dangerous to have an operation at all. Lister's contribution was to cover everything in the operating theatre with carbolic acid – the walls, the floor, all clothing, the surgeon, the anaesthetist, the nurses, the patient, the dressings and the instruments. The staff suffered from carbolic acid poisoning, but the effect was a dramatic fall in sepsis. Later came asepsis, where everything that came in contact with the patient had been previously sterilised. Lister was surgeon to Queen Victoria and President of the Royal Society from 1895 to 1900.

David Lloyd George, later Earl Lloyd-George of Dwyfor, OM (1863–1945), was a Liberal statesman. He served as Chancellor of the Exchequer from 1908 to 1915, during which time he introduced two major reforming acts, the Old Age Pensions Act of 1908 and the National Insurance Act of 1911. He served as Prime Minister from 1916 to 1922, and by his drive was largely instrumental in Britain's winning World War I.

Lumleian Lectures at the Royal College of Physicians of London were founded in 1583 by John Lumley, first Baron Lumley (c 1534–1609).

Sir William MacArthur, KCB, DSO, FRCP (1884–1964), was Director-General of the Army Medical Services and Professor of Tropical Medicine at the Royal Army Medical College.

Sir Robert McCarrison, CIE, FRCP (1878–1960), a major-general in the Indian medical service, was an authority on nutrition. In World War II he was deputy regional adviser in the emergency medical service at Oxford.

Thomas Babington Macaulay, later Lord Macaulay (1800–1859), was an essayist, poet, historian, barrister and politician.

Sir William MacCormac, KCB, KCVO (1836–1901), was surgeon to St Thomas's Hospital. He was President of the Royal College of Surgeons, 1896–1900.

Malcolm Macdonald (1901–1981), the son of Ramsay Macdonald, was Minister of Health in 1940. He later served as a Governor-General and High Commissioner in various parts of the Commonwealth.

Ramsay Macdonald (1866–1937) became Britain's first Labour Prime Minister in 1924. He was Labour Prime Minister again in 1929, and formed a coalition government in 1931, resigning in 1935.

Sir Robert Macintosh (1897–1989) was the first Nuffield Professor of Anaesthetics at Oxford and the first professor of this subject in the British Commonwealth.

Hugh Maclean, FRCP (1879–1957), was the first director of the Professorial Medical Unit and professor of medicine at St Thomas's Hospital. I was his deputy director.

Anthony Mavrogordato (1874–1944) was a physiologist who worked in South Africa on silicosis and tuberculosis.

Richard Mead, FRCP (1673–1754), was the leading physician of his day. He was physician to St Thomas's Hospital and to George II. He declined the Presidency of the Royal College of Physicians. He was a wealthy collector of books and works of art. The Mead Medal was founded in his memory.

Gregor Mendel (1822–1884) was an Austrian monk, biologist and botanist who founded the study of heredity. His work is the basis of the modern science of genetics.

Henry Miller, FRCP (1913–1976), was a neurologist at Newcastle-upon-Tyne. He was noted for his energy and wit. He later became vice-chancellor of the University of Newcastle.

John Chassar Moir, FRCS (1900–1977), was the first Nuffield Professor of Obstetrics and Gynaecology at Oxford.

Charles Moran, later Lord Moran, FRCP (1882–1977), was physician and for 25 years Dean of the medical school at St Mary's Hospital, London, whose reputation he greatly enhanced. He was President of the Royal College of Physicians of London from 1941 to 1950, and had much to do with the genesis of the National Health Service. He was physician to Winston Churchill.

Berkeley George Andrew Moynihan, later Lord Moynihan, KCMG, CB, FRCS (1865–1936), was surgeon at Leeds General Hospital for 20 years, and became known as the finest surgeon in England. He was President of the Royal College of Surgeons, 1926–1932.

Sir Isaac Newton, PRS (1642–1727), scientist and mathematician, discovered the law of gravity. He was President of the Royal Society for 25 years.

Florence Nightingale, OM (1820–1910), reformed the profession of nursing. She went to Scutari in Turkey during the Crimean War of

1853–1856, where she saved hundreds of soldiers' lives by improving hospital care and sanitary conditions. She later advised the army on hospital reform.

Viscount Nuffield (William Morris), CH, GBE (1871–1963), amassed a fortune by the mass production of cars in Britain. He was a philanthropist, especially to medicine.

Sir William Osler, Bart, FRCP, FRS (1849–1919), was a Canadian physician who became professor of medicine at Pennsylvania, then professor at Johns Hopkins, Baltimore, and in 1904 was appointed Regius Professor of Medicine at Oxford. He wrote *The Principles and Practice of Medicine* (1892), which became the best known textbook of medicine in the English-speaking world. He was a 'character' and the most eminent physician of his day.

Sir Max Page, KBE, FRCS (1882–1961), was surgeon to St Thomas's Hospital, and consulting surgeon to the army and the Metropolitan Police.

Sir William Petty (1623–1687) is chiefly remembered as an economist, but his remarkable career included service at sea, teaching anatomy at Oxford and music at Gresham College, London, and surveying in Ireland. He invented a copying machine and a special sea boat.

Sir George Pickering, FRCP, FRS (1904–1980), was a noted clinical scientist, Professor of Medicine at St Mary's Hospital and from 1956 Regius Professor of Medicine at Oxford. On retirement from that chair he became the Master of Pembroke College, Oxford

David Pyke, CBE, FRCP (born 1921), was physician to King's College Hospital, an authority on diabetes and for many years Registrar of the Royal College of Physicians of London.

Rockefeller Foundation was started in 1913 from a gift by John D. Rockefeller (1839–1937), the American oil millionaire. It has made massive donations to the arts, science and medicine.

Sir Humphry Rolleston, Bart, GCVO, KCB, FRCP (1862–1944), was physician to St George's Hospital, London, Regius Professor of Physic at Cambridge, and President of the Royal College of Physicians of London from 1922 to 1926. He was a writer, historian and bibliographer.

Sir Percy Sargent, FRCS (1873–1933), was surgeon to St Thomas's Hospital.

Samuel George Scott (died 1918) was a pathologist who qualified in 1902. He was killed in action during World War I.

Sir Charles Scott Sherrington, GBE, OM, FRS (1857–1952), shared the 1932 Nobel Prize for medicine with Edgar Douglas Adrian (later Lord Adrian) for their work on the central nervous system, which led to new research in its physiology. He was Wayneflete Professor of Physiology at Oxford from 1913 to 1935.

Sir Arthur Stanley (1869–1947) was a son of the 16th Earl of Derby. He was a philanthropist. From 1917 to 1943 he was Treasurer of St Thomas's Hospital.

George Stephenson (1781–1848) was a pioneer railway engineer who designed the prize-winning locomotive *Rocket*.

Arthur Thomson, FRCS (1858–1935), was professor of anatomy at Oxford and at the Royal Academy.

Seymour Graves Toller, MRCP (1867–1902), was an assistant physician to St Thomas's Hospital but had to resign because of ill health. He then became a physician in Cairo and professor of medicine In his memory a prize was founded at St Thomas's.

Sir Douglas Veale (1891–1973) was Registrar of the University of Oxford. He was a civil servant who had been secretary to five Ministers of Health. Although the servant of the university, he had considerable influence on its affairs. Not for nothing was the registry known as the Hôtel de Veale.

Sir Cuthbert Wallace, FRCS (1867–1944), was surgeon to St Thomas's Hospital and Dean of its medical school. During World War I he was a major-general in the army medical service.

Owen de Wesselow, FRCP (1883–1959), was pathologist and physician to St Thomas's Hospital, and in 1933 was appointed professor of medicine there.

Leslie Witts (1898–1982) was professor of medicine at St Bartholomew's Hospital and the first Nuffield Professor of Medicine at Oxford. He was a specialist on anaemia.

Sir Isaac Wolfson (1897–1991) was a Scots-born businessman and philanthropist. He founded the Wolfson Foundation in 1955 and Wolfson College, Oxford, in 1966. Wolfson College, Cambridge, founded in 1965 as University College, was renamed after receiving a large grant from the foundation.

Sir Christopher Wren, FRS (1632–1723), was a professor of astronomy turned architect who designed St Paul's Cathedral and 52 London churches. He was a founder of the Royal Society and President 1680–1682.

Henry Yellowlees, OBE, FRCP (1888–1971) was consulting physician on mental diseases to St Thomas's Hospital.

Publications by A. M. Cooke

An examination paper on Osler, *St Thomas's Hospital Gazette*, 1927

Ping Pong, *St Thomas's Hospital Gazette*, 1927

Some problems in medicine, *St Thomas's Hospital Gazette*, 1931

Observations on alkalosis, *Quarterly Journal of Medicine*, 1931

Alkalosis occurring in the treatment of peptic ulcers, *Quarterly Journal of Medicine*, 1932

Calcification of the kidneys in pyloric stenosis, *Quarterly Journal of Medicine*, 1933

The prognosis of peptic ulcers, *Proceedings of the Royal Society of Medicine*, 1934

Symptomatology of insulin hypoglycaemia, *Lancet*, 1934

Leonardo da Vinci, *St Thomas's Hospital Gazette*, 1935

Measurement of the circulation rate in man, *Proceedings of the Physiological Society*, 1935

Observations on the treatment of myasthenia gravis, *Quarterly Journal of Medicine*, 1936

Alkalosis occurring in the treatment of peptic ulcer, *British Encyclopaedia of Medical Practice*, 1936

Measurement of the cardiac output in man, *Journal of Physiology*, 1937

What can be done to prevent the patient from relapsing? *British Journal of Tuberculosis*, 1938

The Radcliffe Infirmary Handbook, 1940 (and two subsequent editions)

Notes for diabetic patients, 1941 (and three subsequent editions)

Carbohydrate food table, 1941 (and three subsequent editions)

Radcliffe Infirmary diabetic clinic, *Diabetic Journal*, 1942

Homologous serum jaundice, *Lancet*, 1942

Peritoneoscopy, *Lancet*, 1943

Peritoneoscopy, *Proceedings of the Royal Society of Medicine*, 1943

The treatment of coronary artery disease, *Medical Press*, 1943

The treatment of coronary artery disease, *Modern Treatment Year Book*, 1944

A clinical school at Oxford, *Oxford Magazine*, 1945

Ulcerative colitis, *Practitioner*, 1946

Unusual complications of herpes zoster, *Journal of Neurology, Neurosurgery & Psychiatry*, 1949

Pneumonia and empyema due to *S. oranienberg*, *Lancet*, 1949

Temporal arteritis, *Lancet*, 1951

The family doctor and diabetic coma, *British Medical Journal*, 1951

Anticoagulants in myocardial infarction, *British Medical Journal*, 1953

L'instruzione del diabetico, *Giornale dei Diabetici*, 1953

La instruzione de diabetici, *Diabetes* (Montevideo)

Pilocarpine as an antagonist to unwanted effects of ganglion blocking agents in the treatment of hypertension, *British Medical Journal*, 1954

Osteoporosis, *Lancet*, 1955

1907–1957, Jubilee of the Quarterly Journal of Medicine, *Quarterly Journal of Medicine*, 1957

Ageing, *Transactions of the Medical Society of London*, 1957

Backache from organic disease (excluding gynaecological causes), *Practitioner*, 1957

The mystery of Hurdis House, *Oxford Medical School Gazette*, 1959

Fracture patterns, *Lancet*, 1959

Enzymes, *Proceedings of the Royal Society of Medicine*, 1962

Diabetic children of diabetic couples, *British Medical Journal*, 1966

Daniel Whistler, PRCP, *Journal of the Royal College of Physicians*, 1967

The College and Europe, *Journal of the Royal College of Physicians*, 1970

A History of the Royal College of Physicians of London, Volume 3, 1971

Then and now, *Oxford Medical School Gazette*, 1972

The presidents, *Royal College of Physicians Commentary*, 1973

John Caius, 1510–1573, *Journal of the Royal College of Physicians*, 1973

Out of school, *Journal of the Royal College of Physicians*, 1974

The Royal College of Physicians, 1974 (also in French and German)

William Harvey at Oxford, *Journal of the Royal College of Physicians*, 1975

Sir Farquhar Buzzard, Bart, a biography, 1975

Report of General Medical Council Conference, 1975

William Osler and the Royal College of Physicians, 300th meeting of the Osler Club, 1976

Report of the General Medical Council, 1977

A note on Frank Buckland, *Journal of the Royal College of Physicians*, 1981

Samuel Clippingdale, *Journal of the Royal College of Physicians*, 1981

Edited and revised *The Royal Society of Medicine Family Medical Guide*, 1980

Introduction to the *Oxford Textbook of Medicine*, 1982

Queen Victoria's medical household, *Medical History*, 1982

Doctors in other walks of life, *Oxford Companion to Medicine*, 1986

Medical Colleges in the UK, *Oxford Companion to Medicine*, 1986

Fringe medicine, cults and quackery, *Oxford Companion to Medicine*, 1986

Sir Hans Sloane and the Philosophical Transactions, *Journal of the Royal College of Physicians*, 1984

Lionel Penrose, in the *Dictionary of National Biography*, 1986

Introduction to the *Oxford Textbook of Medicine* 2nd edn, 1987

Leslie Witts, in the *Dictionary of National Biography*, 1990

The Cooke's Tale, 1991 (private publication)

St Thomas's Hospital, 1921–1932, *St Thomas's Hospital Gazette*, 1993

Also letters to *The Times, The Lancet, British Medical Journal* and numerous obituaries of medical colleagues, book reviews and other miscellania.

An examination paper on Osler

(4th Edition)

Here is the text of *An Examination Paper on Osler*, by Leonard Dudgeon, Anthony Mavrogordato, and Samuel George Scott, reproduced from the *St Thomas's Hospital Gazette* of 1902.

There seems to be a certain monotony about medical examinations, so we suggest the following, by way of variety.

1. Who was Mephibosheth? What parental superstition dates from his time?

2. What is 'one of the saddest chapters in the history of human deception'?

3. Give Osler's quotations from the following authors: John Bunyan, Byron, John Chiene, Montaigne. Explain the context where necessary.

4. Describe, if necessary with the aid of diagrams, Kemp's double current rectal tubes. What are the indications for their employment?

5. Give in full the name of 'the distinguished old Bath physician.' At what period did he flourish, and what is his claim to distinction?

6. As a sequence to what therapeutic procedure did the son of Professor Langerhans die? What was the pathological and medico-legal interest of the case?

7. What is the chief recorded complication of a lay committee meeting at St George's Hospital?

8. Who was convinced that more wise men than fools are victims of gout? Is there any reason why he, in particular, should hold that view?

9. What cases drift to 'museums and side-shows'?

10. How did Trousseau's patient make money?

11. What celebrated English physician preferred to die in harness? State the cause of death.

12. What internal evidence is there:

   a) That Osler has had an unhappy experience with cheap bicycles?
   b) That he is interested in the history of Napoleon Buonaparte?

13. What is O. Rosenbach's dictum on the custom of wearing stays?

14. Give the context of the following quotations and make explanatory remarks if needed:
   a) Cases are given after nearly every one of the specific fevers.
   b) I saw, some years ago, one of the most distinguished gynaecologists of Germany perform laparotomy in a case of this kind.
   c) The doses given by the late Alonzo Clark, of New York, may be truly termed heroic.
   d) In a somewhat varied post-mortem and clinical experience, no instance has fallen under my observation.
   e) A history of gorging with peanuts.
   f) I have seen Murchison himself in doubt.
   g) A toad-like caricature of humanity.
   h) From the accurate view of Laennec and Louis the profession was led away by Graves and particularly by Niemeyer.
   i) One of the most powerful enemies of the American stomach at the present day.
   j) I had a lesson in this matter which I have never forgotten.

15. Who was Van Helmont, and when did he live? Give a brief account of his opinions on contemporary medicine.

16. Who made an autopsy on Dean Swift, and what did he report?

17. What interest attaches to:
   a) The Pullman car conductor from Chicago?
   b) The Appleton-Swain family?
   c) Yellow cakes at Philadelphia?
   d) Chancellor Ferrier?
   e) Master McGrath?
   f) Renforth, the oarsman?
   g) Shattock's patient?

18. Who had a translucent head? What was the pathology of the condition?

19. On what occasion was a surgeon entrapped by a neurotic physician?

ANSWERS

1. Mephibosheth was the son of Jonathan and grandson of Saul. His parents attributed his lameness to his having been dropped by his nurse.

2. Hysteria and the Salem witches.

3. Bunyan described pneumonia as 'the captain of these men of death.' Byron described corpulence as 'an oily dropsy.' Chiene said 'Eat less after age 50.' Montaigne described an attack of the stone (renal colic).

4. An arrangement of tubes for irrigating the rectum in anuria.

5. Caleb Hillier Parry (1825) described hyperthyroidism.

6. Preventive inoculation with diphtheria antitoxin. ?Thymus.

7. John Hunter's angina.

8. Sydenham on gout. Many distinguished doctors have had it.

9. Patients deformed by progressive muscular atrophy.

10. A man with bulimia was bribed by an eating house not to eat so much (FREE) bread.

11. Hilton Fagge. He died from aneurysm of the aorta.

12. a) 'Entire families sometimes show early arteriosclerosis, a tendency to which cannot be explained in any other way than that in the make-up of the machine bad material was used for the tubing.'
    b) He mentions the Buonaparte family's tendency to cancer, Napoleon's slow pulse, his possible epilepsy and his extraordinary mental and physical vigour.

13. The relation of corsets to chlorosis.

14. a) Thyroid abscess.
    b) Retroperitoneal Hodgkin's disease mistaken for uterine tumours.
    c) Opium in acute peritonitis.
    d) Acute yellow atrophy of the liver.
    e) Appendicitis.
    f) Typhus fever.
    g) Cretinism.
    h) About tuberculosis.
    i) The soda-water fountain.
    j) Typhoid fever.

15. Johannes Van Helmont (1577–1644) was against bleeding as a treatment. He said that 'a Bloody Moloch presides in the Chairs of Medicine.'

16. Mr Whiteway. Hydrocephalus.

17. a) He carried smallpox from Chicago to Montreal.
    b) Haemophilia, 400 years and 13 generations.
    c) Lead poisoning.
    d) Had an irregular pulse for 50 years and lived to be 88.
    e) A famous greyhound, had a large heart. So did Eclipse, the famous racehorse.
    f) Died during a rowing race.
    g) He had Sable intestinal, that is vegetable debris in the faeces.

18. A man called Cardinal who had chronic hydrocephalus and a translucent head.

19. A doctor who mimicked the symptoms and faked the signs of appendicitis.

A test of knowledge

This is the text of the paper based on the work of Sir William Osler which appeared in the *King's College Hospital Gazette* of 1920:

A TEST OF KNOWLEDGE

Fortified by the concentrated efforts of the K.C.H Staff, I entered the Examination Hall with a feeling of confidence, but the complacent smile with which I received the paper from the hands of the Examiner speedily changed to something resembling the risus sardonicus.

Rising from my bench, I approached the Examiner. 'Sir,' said I, 'not being a student of International History, may I have your permission to retire as I find I have entered the wrong examination room?' 'Of what subject are you a student?' he asked. 'Of medicine, Sir.' 'Then your remark reveals ignorance,' he replied. 'For the answers to all these questions are to be found in a well-known text book, the 8th edition of The Principles and Practice of Medicine by Sir William Osler.'

In dismay I left the room as the questions were quite beyond the extent of my knowledge. Here is the paper, and I propose to spend the interval, until I can again present myself before the Examiners, in looking up the answers.

1. *Who were*:
   Blue Mary, the Friend of the Aged, Master McGrath, the Captain of the Men of Death, Jumping Frenchmen, the Salem Witches?

2. *Criticize the advice given by*:
   Eryximachus to Aristophanes, Rondibilis to Panurge and the treatment of the son of Edward I by John of Gaddesden.

3. *Adduce evidence to show that*:
   a) Sir William Osler moved in the upper circles.
   b) The state of suspended animation during which the Master of Ballantrae was buried by Secundra, was not entirely an invention on the part of R. L. Stevenson.

4. *State*:
   The pulse rate of Napoleon, the weight of George Cheyne, the indication for splenectomy in athletes, the reason why attention was paid to the oyster and what the governess taught the children.

5. *What are*:
   The Black Death, the blue disease, the green sickness, the raspberry tongue, the mulberry rash, the lazy disease, the beefsteak hand and the calamity of sailors?

6. *Give the context of*:
   'A Physician with a belly ache'; 'Whose head was translucent when the sun was shining behind him'; 'A medical student while on the spree.'

7. *From what illnesses did the following suffer?*
   Sydenham, Hartley Coleridge, Sir William Osler, Julius Caesar, the first Lord Shaftesbury and the son of the Shunamite woman.
   And from what did the following die?
   George Washington, Father Damien, Hilton Fagge, Dean Swift, and Charcot

8. *Who said*:
   'Shut your mouth and save your life'; 'He cures most successfully in whom people have the greatest confidence'; 'A Bloody Moloch presides in the Chairs of Medicine'; 'Milk and sweet sound blood differ in nothing but colour'? To what were they referring?

The answers to these questions appeared in the next issue of the *Gazette* in the form of the numbers of the pages where they appeared.

An examination on Osler

This is the paper based on the tenth edition of Osler's great work that Walter Chiesman, John Taylor, and I published in the *St Thomas's Hospital Gazette* in 1927:

AN EXAMINATION ON OSLER

1. What was the cause of death in the following:
   a) George Washington?
   b) Louis XV?
   c) Sir Robert Darcy?
   d) Ignatius Loyola?
   e) Marcus Aurelius?

2. What did the following suffer from:
   a) Morgagni's 15 children
   b) The astronomer Airy?
   c) Montaigne?
   d) The first Lord Shaftesbury?
   e) Charcot, Nothnagel and Pepper?

3. What interest attaches to:
   a) The son of the Shunamite woman?
   b) The Crimean veteran who died at Toronto in 1885?
   c) Sarah Nelmes and James Phipps?
   d) The top of Pike's Peak?
   e) Montana and Idaho?

4. What was the good news that Dickinson gave to the drinking classes?

5. What disease should always be suspected when a large party among Germans is followed by cases of apparent typhoid fever?

6. What was the reckless act of a medical student while on a spree?

7. To what do the following passages refer?
   a) 'There has been no more remarkable triumph of modern hygiene than ...'
   b) 'More wise men than fools are victims of the affection.'
   c) 'A Bloody Moloch presides in the Chairs of Medicine.'

d) 'As St Paul says, "It is better to marry than to burn".'

e) 'As Aretaeus remarks, a person in the interval has won the race at the Olympic games.'

f) 'Perhaps no single affection has brought more discredit on the profession'

g) ' ... the potential energies of the higher constellations of their association centres have been squandered by their ancestors.'

h) ' ... and this, with a little tinge of red in parts, gave the appearance of a polished porphyry or greenstone.'

i) 'The amazing stupidity (which was shared by not a few physicians who should have known better) ... of the Governor of the State of San Francisco.'

8. What illness may be caused by hair dye, false teeth and thread?

9. How did John of Gaddesden treat the son of Edward I?

10. Who was the French Hippocrates?

11. What was Oliver Wendell Holmes's slight ailment which promotes longevity?

12. What did A.E. Russell point out?

13. Who was bled from both arms for haemoptysis?

14. What were the 'Jumping Frenchmen'?

15. Two of the world's greatest generals suffered from the same disease. Who were they? What was it?

16. Who tapped a bladder thinking it to be ascites?

17. Mention some diseases to which Jews are specially prone.

18. What disease did Maudlin sing about in the Compleat Angler?

19. 'A boy aged five was admitted to St Thomas's Hospital with' ... what?

20. Who said 'Do not think, but try, be patient, be accurate', and to whom?

21. What was Napoleon's pulse rate?

22. Where did Dock find the barley-ear and how did it get there?

23. Comment on Osler's use of the Parable of the Sower.

For the benefit of the uninstructed the answers appear below.

1. a) Diphtheria.
   b) Second attack of smallpox.
   c) Rupture of the left ventricle.
   d) Perforation of the gall bladder into the portal vein.
   e) Pesta Magna, probably smallpox.

2. a) Icterus neonatorum.
   b) Migraine.
   c) Renal colic.
   d) Hydatid disease.
   e) Angina pectoris.

3. a) Sunstroke.
   b) Dissecting aneurysm.
   c) First to be vaccinated (14th May 1796)
   d) Study of Mountain Sickness.
   e) Rocky Mountain Spotted Fever. Tick Fever.

4. That the effects of alcohol on the kidneys have been much overrated.

5. Trichiniasis.

6. Passed a pin into his heart.

7. a) Takagi's dietetic reforms in the Japanese navy (Beri beri).
   b) Gout.
   c) Van Helmont on bleeding as a treatment.
   d) Syphilis and sexual continence.
   e) Acute gout.
   f) Hysteria.
   g) Neurasthenia.
   h) Richard Bright's description of the nephritic kidney.
   i) Plague.

8. Lead poisoning.

9. Wrapped him in red flannel.

10. Ballonius (1538–1616).

11. Mild asthma.

12. Danger of exploratory puncture of the lung.

13. Laurence Sterne.

14. Saltatory spasm. In Maine and Canada.

15. Julius Caesar and Napoleon. Epilepsy.

16. John Hunter.

17. Diabetes mellitus, angina pectoris, Tay Sachs disease, pediculosis.

18. Chlorosis, not common in country girls.

19. Smallpox.

20. William Hunter—to Edward Jenner.

21. 40.

22. In the liver. It was swallowed and got through the oesophageal wall.

23. He applied it to the aetiology of tuberculosis.

Index